CW00670350

EASIEST KEYBOARD COLLECTION

Top Pop Chart Hits

WISE PUBLICATIONS
London/New York/Paris/Sydney/Copenhagen/Berlin/Madrid/Tokyo

Exclusive Distributors:

Music Sales Limited
8/9 Frith Street,
London W1D 3JB, England.

Music Sales Pty Limited
120 Rothschild Avenue,
Rosebery, NSW 2018,
Australia.

Order No. AM972081
ISBN 0-7119-9087-5
This book © Copyright 2002 by Wise Publications

Compiled by Nick Crispin
Music arranged by Roger Day & Derek Jones
Music processed by Paul Ewers Music Design
Cover design by Chloë Alexander
Printed and bound in Malta.

Your Guarantee of Quality
As publishers, we strive to produce every book to the highest
commercial standards.
This book has been carefully designed to minimise awkward page
turns and to make playing from it a real pleasure.
Particular care has been given to specifying acid-free, neutral-sized
paper made from pulps which have not been elemental chlorine
bleached. This pulp is from farmed sustainable forests and was
produced with special regard for the environment.
Throughout, the printing and binding have been planned to
ensure a sturdy, attractive publication which should give years
of enjoyment.
If your copy fails to meet our high standards, please inform us
and we will gladly replace it.

www.musicsales.com

Contents

THE AIR THAT I BREATHE

Words & Music by Albert Hammond & Mike Hazelwood

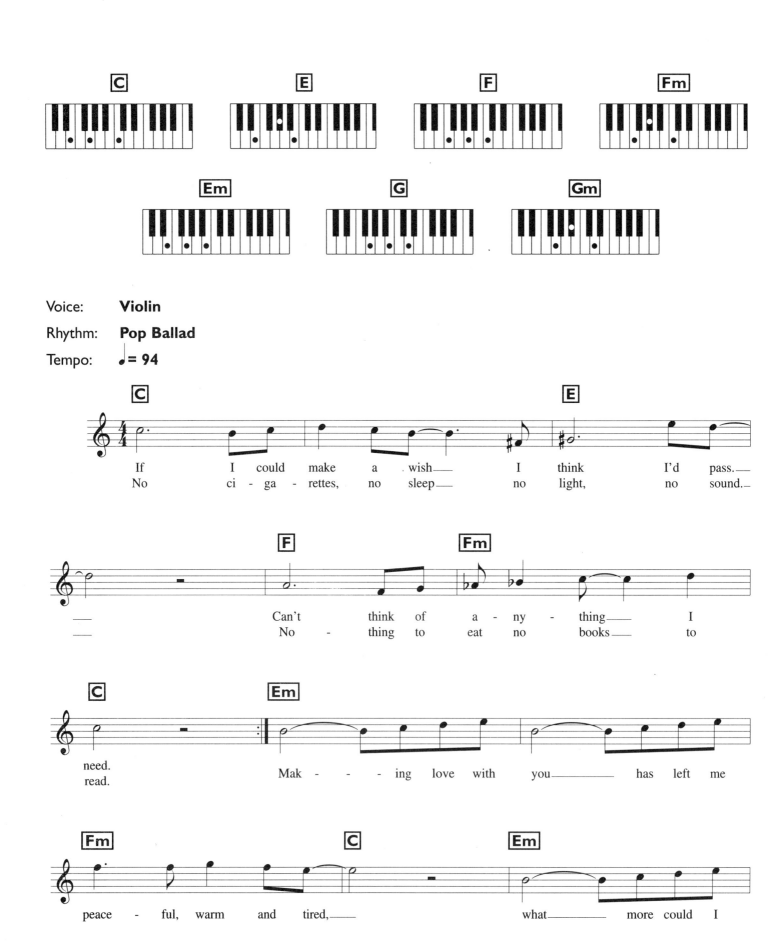

Voice: **Violin**

Rhythm: **Pop Ballad**

Tempo: ♩ = 94

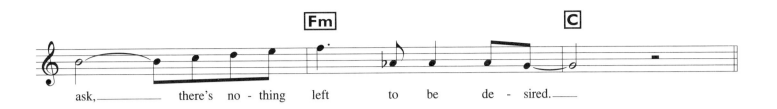

ask,_____ there's no - thing left to be de - sired._____

Peace came up - on me and it leaves me weak,____

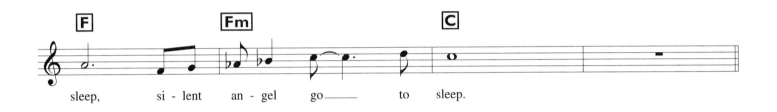

sleep, si - lent an - gel go_____ to sleep.

Some - times,____ all I need is the air____ that I breathe__ and to

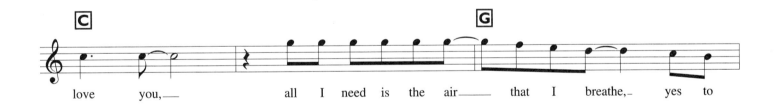

love you,____ all I need is the air____ that I breathe,_ yes to

love you,____ all I need is the air_____ that I breathe._

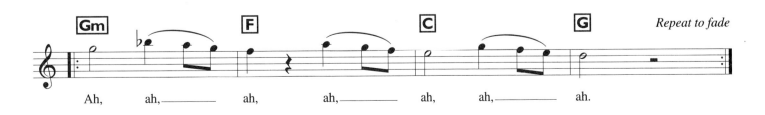

Ah, ah,_____ ah, ah,____ ah, ah,_____ ah.

ALWAYS ON MY MIND

Words & Music by Wayne Thompson, Mark James & Johnny Christopher

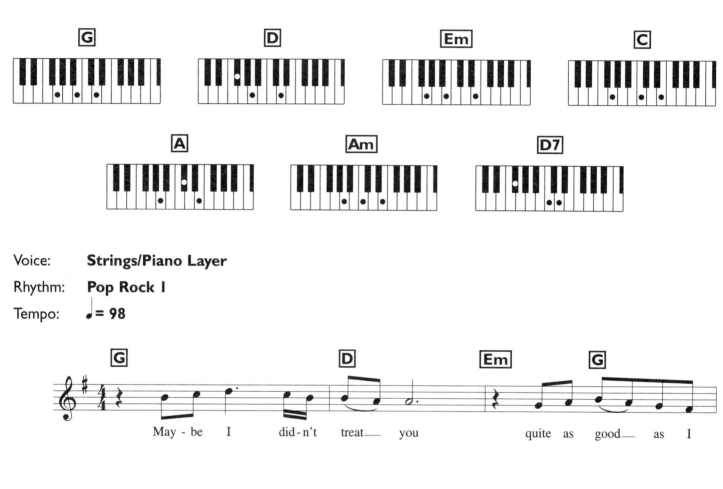

Voice: **Strings/Piano Layer**

Rhythm: **Pop Rock I**

Tempo: ♩ = 98

May - be I did - n't treat____ you quite as good____ as I

should have, may - be I did - n't love____ you

quite as of - ten as I should____ have. Lit - tle things I should have

said and done, I just nev - er took the time.____

You were al-ways on my mind, you were al-ways on my mind.

May-be I did-n't hold— you all those lone-ly, lone-ly times,

and I guess I nev-er told— you, I'm so hap-py that you're

mine._____ If I made you feel— se - cond best,

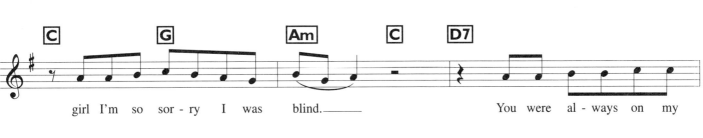

girl I'm so sor-ry I was blind._____ You were al-ways on my

mind, you were al-ways on my mind.

You were al-ways on my mind.

ANGELS

Words & Music by Robbie Williams & Guy Chambers

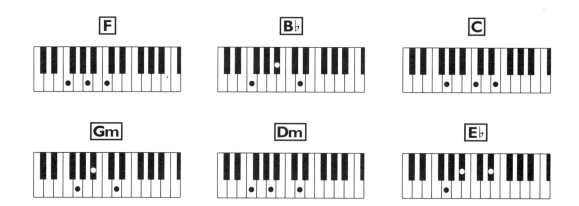

Voice: **Studio Piano**

Rhythm: **Pop Ballad**

Tempo: ♩ = 74

I sit and wait,___ does an an -

- gel con - tem - plate___ my fate?___ And do they know___

___ the pla - ces where___ we go___ when we're grey and old?___

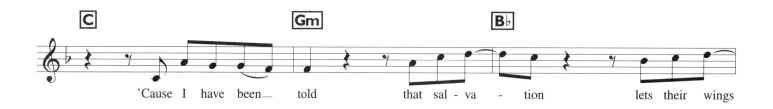

'Cause I have been___ told that sal - va - tion lets their wings

_____ un - fold._____ So when I'm ly - ing in my bed, thoughts

run-ning through my head, and I feel that love is dead, _____

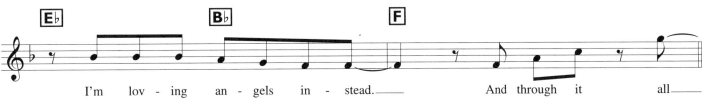

I'm lov - ing an - gels in - stead._____ And through it all_____

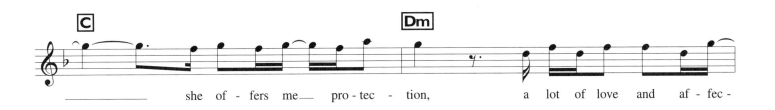

_____ she of - fers me_____ pro - tec - tion, a lot of love and af - fec -

- tion whe-ther I'm right or wrong. And down the wa - ter - fall,_____ wher-ev-er it_____ may take_____

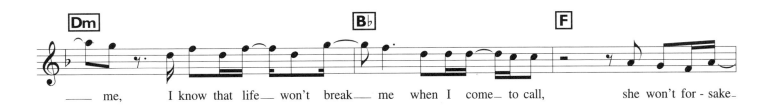

_____ me, I know that life_____ won't break_____ me when I come_____ to call, she won't for - sake_____

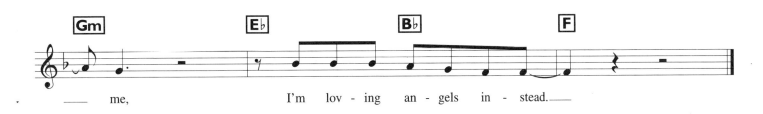

_____ me, I'm lov - ing an - gels in - stead._____

BAKER STREET

Words & Music by Gerry Rafferty

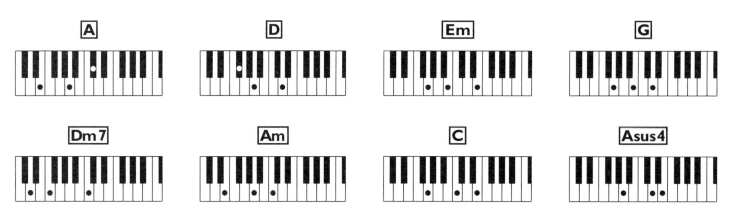

Voice: **Acoustic Guitar**

Rhythm: **Folky Pop**

Tempo: ♩ = 120

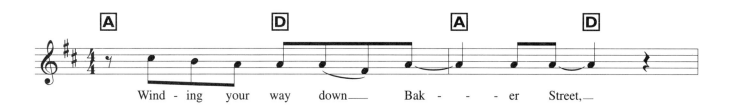

Wind - ing your way down___ Bak - - - er Street,___

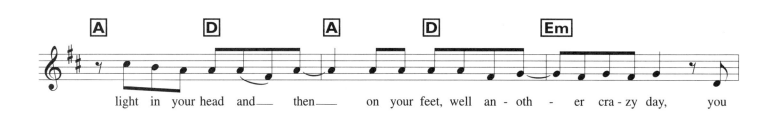

light in your head and___ then___ on your feet, well an - oth - er cra - zy day, you

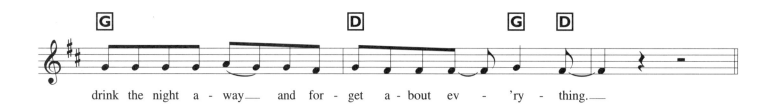

drink the night a - way___ and for - get a - bout ev - 'ry - thing.___

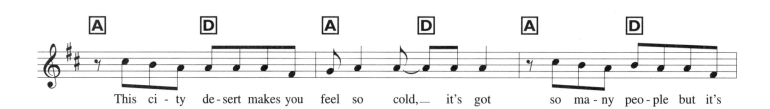

This ci - ty de - sert makes you feel so cold,___ it's got so ma - ny peo - ple but it's

got no soul— and it's tak - en me so long— to find out you were wrong,— when you

sort-ed out ev - 'ry - thing.— You used to think that it was so ea - sy,

you used to say that it was so ea - sy but you're try - ing, you're try - ing now.—

An - oth-er year and then you'll be hap - py, just one more year and then you'll

be hap - py, but you're cry - ing, you're cry - ing now.—

Repeat to fade

11

BLOWIN' IN THE WIND

Words & Music by Bob Dylan

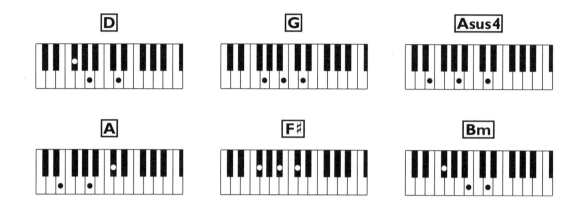

Voice: **Studio Piano**

Rhythm: **Folklore**

Tempo: ♩ = 164

How ma - ny roads must___ a man walk___

down be - fore you call him___ a

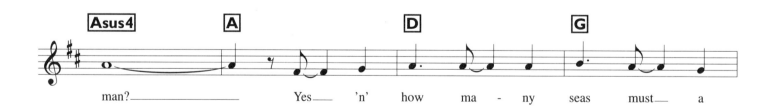

man?___ Yes___ 'n' how ma - ny seas must___ a

white dove___ sail be - fore she sweeps in___ the

sand?_____ Yes_____ 'n' how ma - ny

times must_____ the can - non - balls_____ fly be -

- fore they're__ for - ev - er banned?_____ The

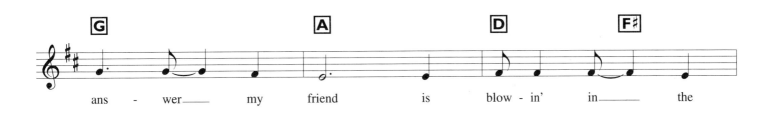

ans - wer_____ my friend is blow - in' in_____ the

wind, the ans - wer____ is blow - in' in_____ the

wind._____ The ans - wer___ is blow - in' in_____ the

wind._____

CALL ME

Words & Music by Tony Hatch

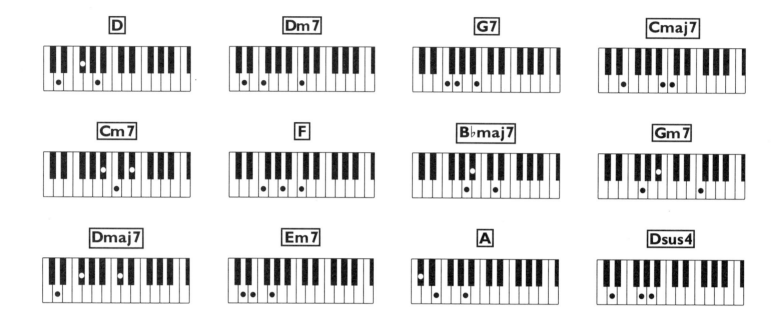

Voice: **Piano**

Rhythm: **Ska**

Tempo: ♩ = 126

If you're feel-ing sad___ and lone - ly, there's a ser-vice I___ can ren - der,

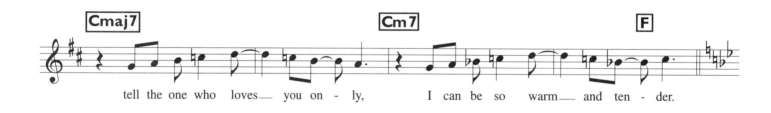

tell the one who loves___ you on - ly, I can be so warm___ and ten - der.

Call me, don't be a - fraid,___ you can call me, may - be it's late,___ but just

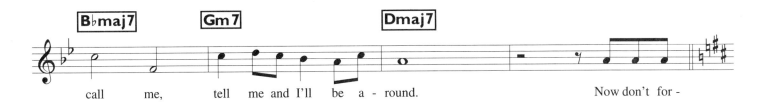

call me, tell me and I'll be a - round. Now don't for -

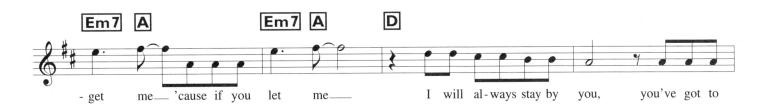

- get me— 'cause if you let me— I will al-ways stay by you, you've got to

trust me,—that's how it must be,— there's so much that I can do.—

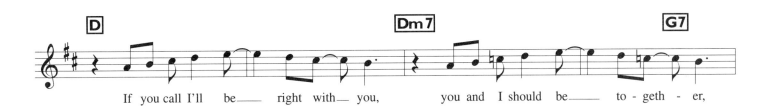

If you call I'll be— right with— you, you and I should be— to - geth - er,

with this love I long— to give— you, I'll be at your side— for - ev - er.

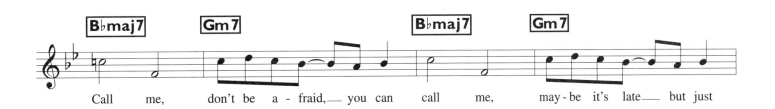

Call me, don't be a - fraid,— you can call me, may - be it's late— but just

Repeat to fade

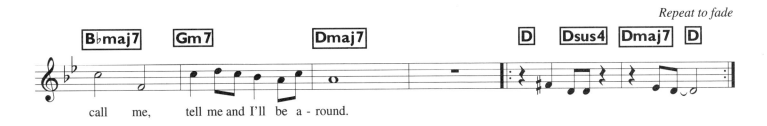

call me, tell me and I'll be a - round.

CARS

Words & Music by Gary Numan

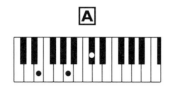 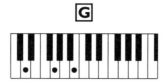 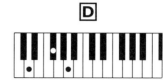

Voice: **Strings/Electric Piano Split**

Rhythm: **16 Beat Pop**

Tempo: ♩ = **126**

Here in my car   I feel saf-est of all.   I can lock up my doors,   it's the

on - ly way to live, in cars.

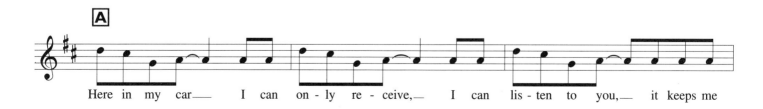

Here in my car   I can on-ly re-ceive,   I can lis-ten to you,   it keeps me

sta - ble for nights in cars.

Here in my car where the i - mage breaks down, will you vi - sit me, please, if I

op - en my door in cars. Here in my car I know I've

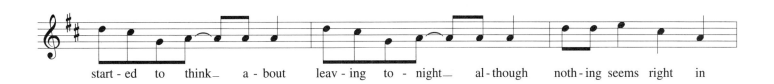

start - ed to think a - bout leav - ing to - night al - though noth - ing seems right in

cars.

Repeat to fade

DIZZY

Words & Music by Tommy Roe & Freddy Weller
© Copyright 1969 Low Twi Music Incorporated, USA.
BMG Music Publishing Limited.
All Rights Reserved. International Copyright Secured.

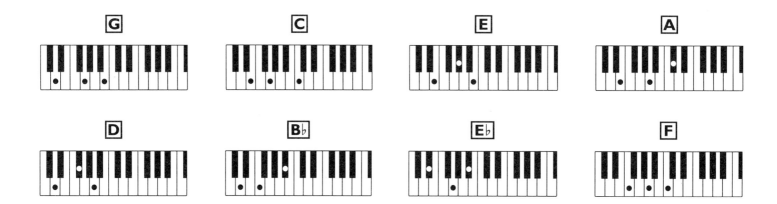

Voice: **Clarinet**

Rhythm: **Pop Ballad**

Tempo: ♩= 104

Diz - zy,   I'm so   diz - zy my head is spin - ning,   like a

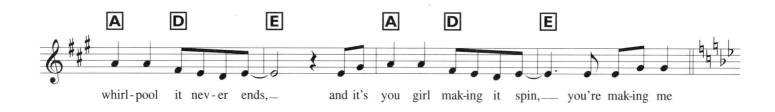

whirl - pool it nev - er ends,—   and it's you girl mak - ing it spin,— you're mak - ing me

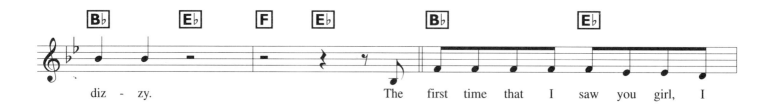

diz - zy.   The first time that I saw you girl, I

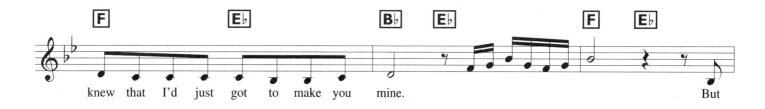

knew that I'd just got to make you mine.   But

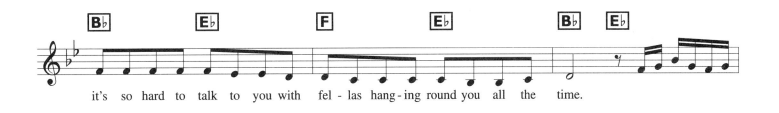

it's so hard to talk to you with fel-las hang-ing round you all the time.

I want you for my sweet babe but you keep play-ing hard to get and I'm

go-ing round in cir-cles all the time. Diz-zy, I'm so

diz-zy my head is spin-ning, like a whirl-pool it nev-er ends,—

— and it's you girl mak-ing it spin,— you're mak-ing me

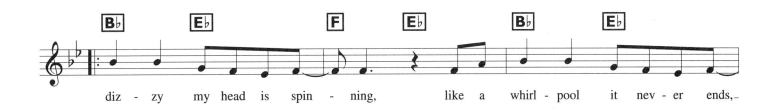

diz-zy my head is spin-ning, like a whirl-pool it nev-er ends,—

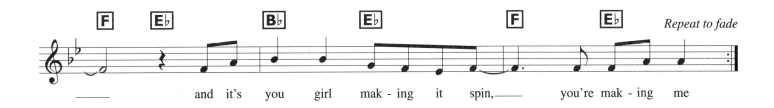

Repeat to fade

— and it's you girl mak-ing it spin,— you're mak-ing me

DON'T CRY FOR ME ARGENTINA

Music by Andrew Lloyd Webber
Lyrics by Tim Rice

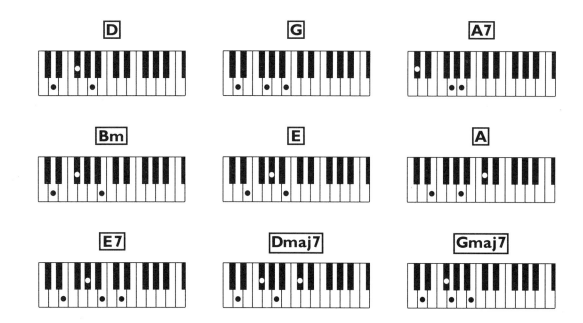

Voice: **Jazz Organ**

Rhythm: **16 Beat**

Tempo: ♩ = 88

It won't be ea - sy, you'll think it

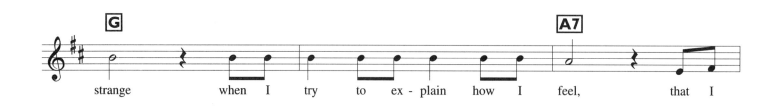

strange when I try to ex - plain how I feel, that I

still need your love af - ter all that I've done. ____ You won't be -

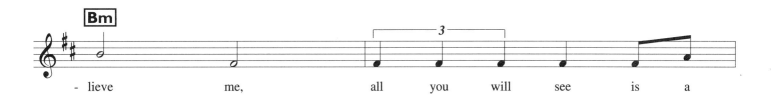

-lieve me, all you will see is a

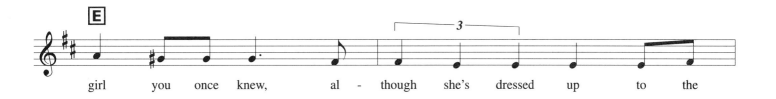

girl you once knew, al - though she's dressed up to the

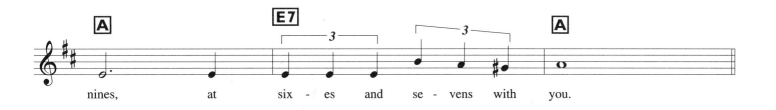

nines, at six - es and se - vens with you.

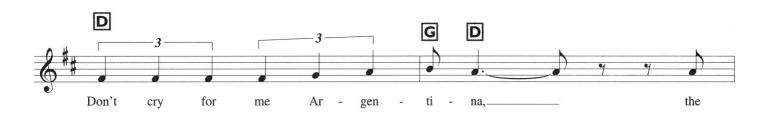

Don't cry for me Ar - gen - ti - na,_____ the

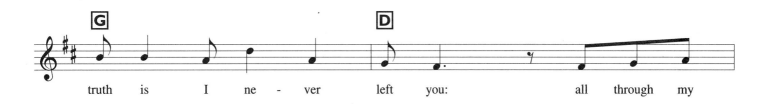

truth is I ne - ver left you: all through my

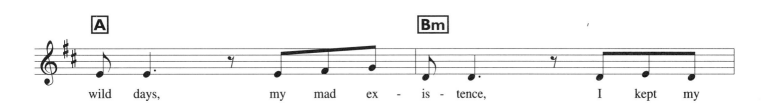

wild days, my mad ex - is - tence, I kept my

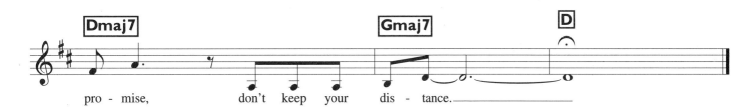

pro - mise, don't keep your dis - tance._____

FIELDS OF GOLD

Words & Music by Sting

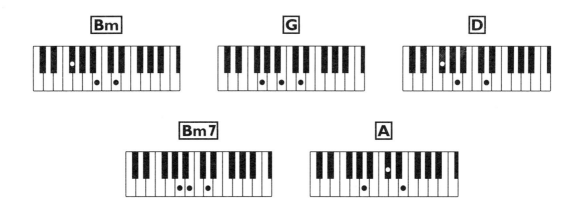

Voice: **Clarinet**

Rhythm: **Soft Rock**

Tempo: ♩ = 96

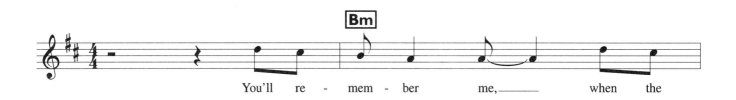

You'll re - mem - ber me,____ when the

west wind moves,____ up - on the fields____ of bar -

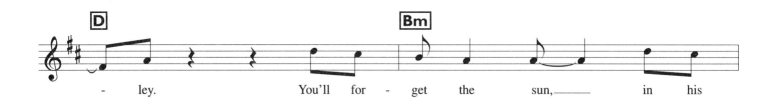

- ley. You'll for - get the sun,____ in his

jea - lous sky,____ as we walk in fields____ of gold.

So she took her love, for to gaze a - while, up -

- on the fields of bar - ley. In his

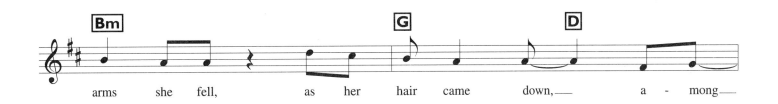

arms she fell, as her hair came down, a - mong

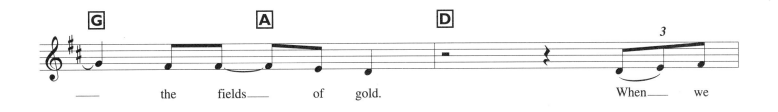

the fields of gold. When we

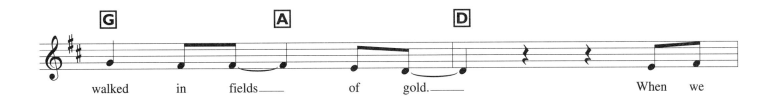

walked in fields of gold. When we

walked in fields of gold.

FLYING WITHOUT WINGS

Words & Music by Steve Mac & Wayne Hector
© Copyright 1999 Rokstone Music / Rondor Music (London) Limited.
All Rights Reserved. International Copyright Secured.

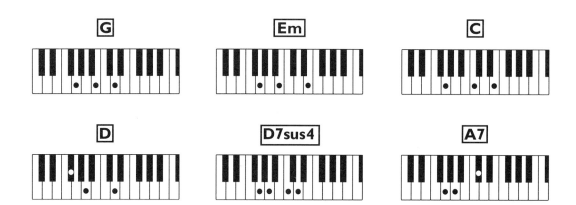

Voice: **Acoustic Guitar**

Rhythm: **Epic Ballad**

Tempo: ♩ = 73

Ev-'ry-bo-dy's look-ing for that some - thing,— one thing that makes it all com -

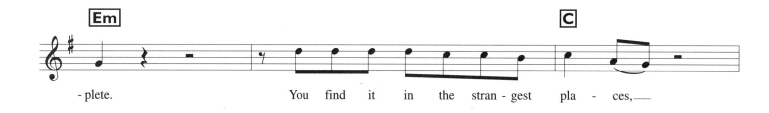

- plete. You find it in the stran - gest pla - ces,—

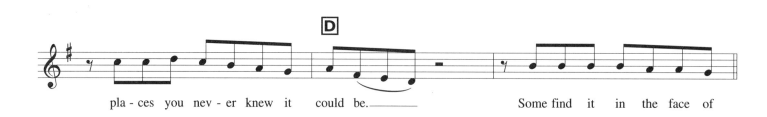

pla - ces you nev - er knew it could be.— Some find it in the face of

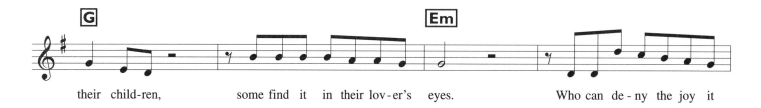

their child - ren, some find it in their lov - er's eyes. Who can de - ny the joy it

brings, when you've found that spe-cial thing? You're fly-ing with-out wings. Some find it shar-ing ev-'ry

morn - ing,___ some in their so - li - ta - ry lives, you find it in the words of

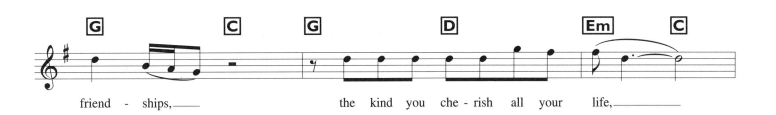

oth - ers,___ a sim-ple line can make you laugh___ or cry. You find it in the deep-est

friend - ships,___ the kind you che-rish all your life,___

and when you know how much that means, you've found that spe-cial thing, I'm fly-ing with-out wings.

And you're the place my life be-gins and you'll be where it ends, I'm fly-ing with-out

wings. And that's the joy you bring, I'm fly-ing with-out wings.

I HAVE A DREAM

Words & Music by Benny Andersson & Björn Ulvaeus

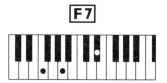
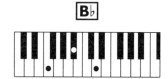
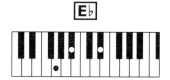
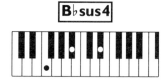

Voice: **Bass/Piano Split**

Rhythm: **Soul Ballad**

Tempo: ♩ = 112

I have a dream, a song to

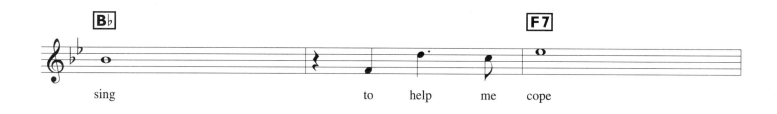

sing to help me cope

with a - ny - thing. If you see the

won - der of a fai - ry tale, you can take the

an - gels, some - thing good in ev - 'ry - thing, I

see, I be - lieve in an - gels, when I know the

time is right for me. I'll cross the stream,

I have a dream. I'll cross the

stream, I have a dream.

Repeat to fade

I JUST WANT TO MAKE LOVE TO YOU

Words & Music by Willie Dixon

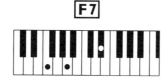
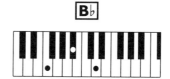

Voice: **Piano 1**

Rhythm: **16 Beat Shuffle**

Tempo: ♩ = 108

I don't want you to be no slave, I don't want you

to work all day. But I want you to be true____ and

I just want to make love____ to you. Love____ to you,

ooh____ ooh,____ love____ to you.

All I want to do is wash your clothes, I don't want to

keep you in-doors. There is no-thing for you to do_____ but

keep me mak - ing love_____ to you. Love _____ to you,

ooh_____ ooh,_____ love_____ to you. And I can

tell by the way you walk that walk, and I can hear by the way you

talk that talk, and I can know by the way you treat your girl that I could

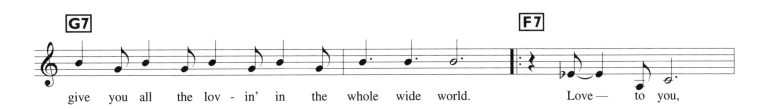

Repeat to fade

give you all the lov - in' in the whole wide world. Love _____ to you,

ooh_____ ooh,_____ love_____ to you.

JEALOUS GUY

Words & Music by John Lennon

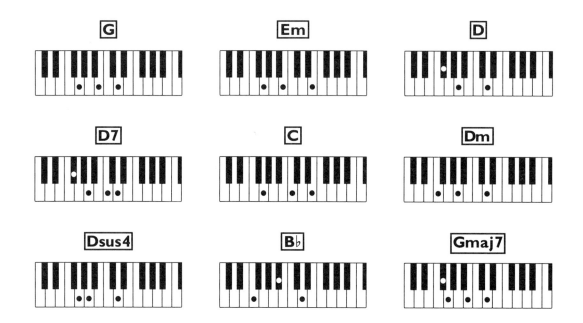

Voice: **Clarinet**

Rhythm: **Rock**

Tempo: ♩ = 80

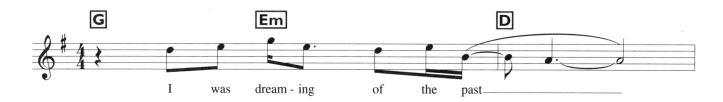

I was dream - ing of the past____

and my heart___ was beat - ing fast.___

I be - gan___ to lose___ con - trol,___

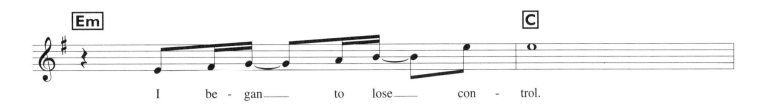

I be-gan___ to lose___ con-trol.

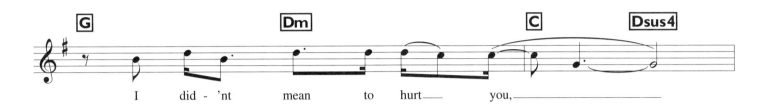

I did-'nt mean to hurt___ you,___

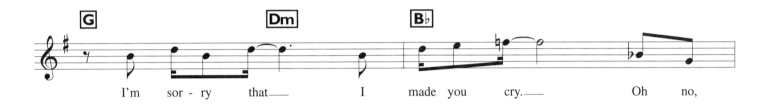

I'm sor-ry that___ I made you cry.___ Oh no,

I did-'nt mean___ to hurt___ you.

I'm just a jea-lous guy,___ watch out I'm just a jea-lous guy,___ look out___ babe,

I'm just a jea-lous guy.___

KEEP ON RUNNING

Words & Music by Jackie Edwards

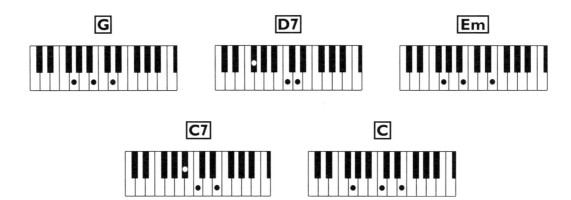

Voice: **Electric Piano**

Rhythm: **4 Beat Rock**

Tempo: ♩ = 128

Keep on run - ning, keep on hid -

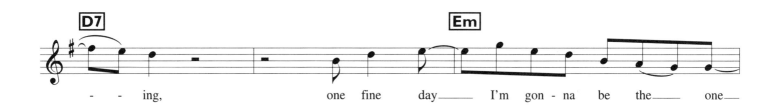

- ing, one fine day ___ I'm gon - na be the ___ one

___ to make you un - der - stand, ___ oh yeah,

___ I'm gon - na be your ___ man. ___ Hey, hey, hey, ___

ev - 'ry - one is talk - ing a - bout me,

it make me feel so bad, hey, hey, hey

ev - 'ry - one is laugh - ing at me,

it make me feel so sad. Oh keep on run -

- ning, run - ning from my arms,

one fine day I'm gon - na be the one to make you un - der - stand,

oh yeah. I'm gon - na be your man.

LAY ALL YOUR LOVE ON ME

Words & Music by Benny Andersson & Björn Ulvaeus

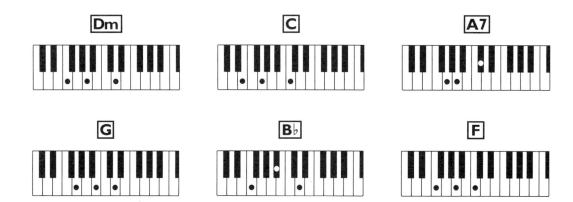

Voice: **Synth. Strings 1**

Rhythm: **Lite Pop**

Tempo: ♩ = 118

I was - n't jea - lous be - fore we met,   now ev - 'ry wo - man I

see is a po - ten - tial threat.   And I'm pos - ses - sive, it

is - n't nice,   you've heard me say - ing that smok - ing was my

on - ly vice.   But now it is - n't true,   now

ev - 'ry - thing is new   and all I've learned—— has

ov - er - turned,—— I beg of you.——

Don't   go   wast - ing your e - mo - - - -

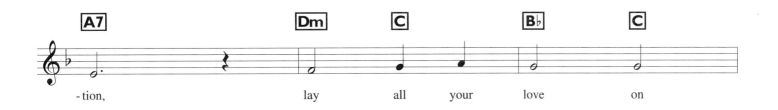

- tion,   lay   all   your   love   on

me.——   Don't   go

shar - ing your de - vo - - - - tion,

Repeat to fade

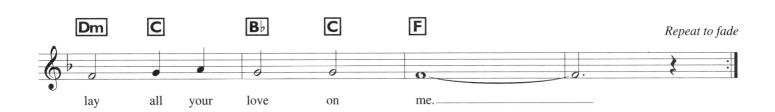

lay   all   your   love   on   me.——

LE FREAK

Words & Music by Bernard Edwards & Nile Rodgers

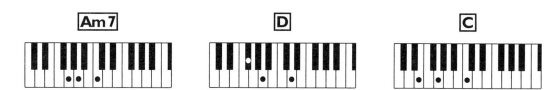

Voice: **Voice Bass**

Rhythm: **Club Bass**

Tempo: ♩ = 120

Freak out, le freak, c'est chic, freak

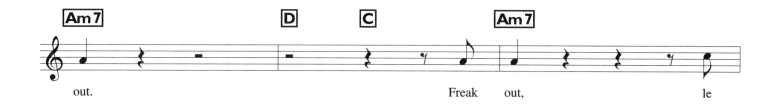

out. Freak out, le

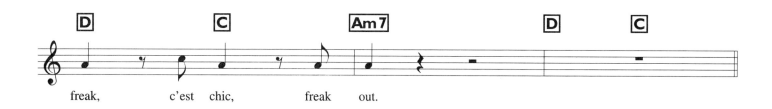

freak, c'est chic, freak out.

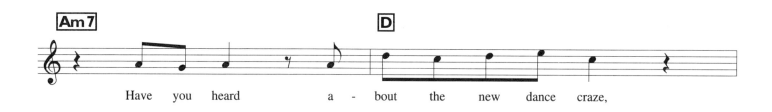

Have you heard a - bout the new dance craze,

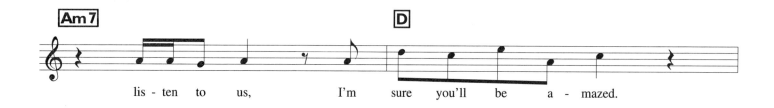

lis - ten to us, I'm sure you'll be a - mazed.

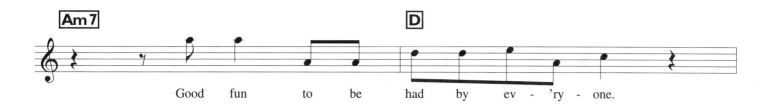

Good fun to be had by ev - 'ry - one.

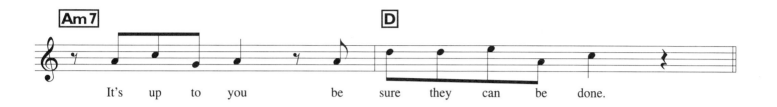

It's up to you be sure they can be done.

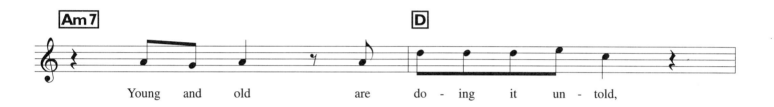

Young and old are do - ing it un - told,

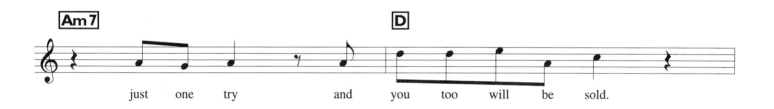

just one try and you too will be sold.

It's all le freak, they're do - in' it night and day,

Bad man - ners will show the way. Freak out, le

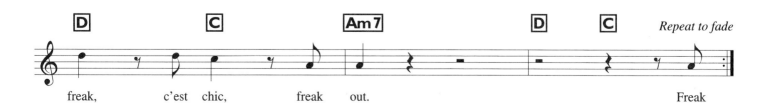

Repeat to fade

freak, c'est chic, freak out. Freak

LET IT BE

Words & Music by John Lennon & Paul McCartney

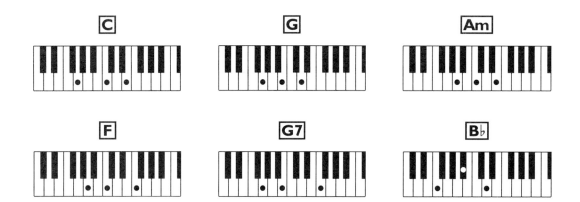

Voice: **Studio Piano**

Rhythm: **Soft Rock I**

Tempo: ♩ = 74

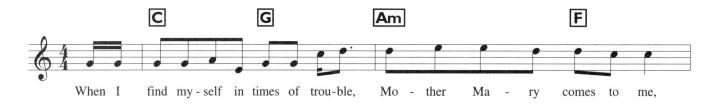

When I find my-self in times of trou-ble, Mo - ther Ma - ry comes to me,

speak-ing words of wis - dom, let it be.___ And

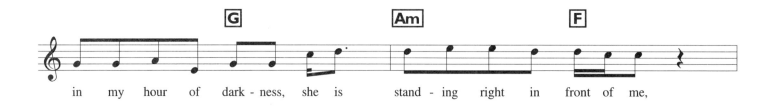

in my hour of dark - ness, she is stand - ing right in front of me,

speak-ing words of wis - dom, let it be.___ Let it

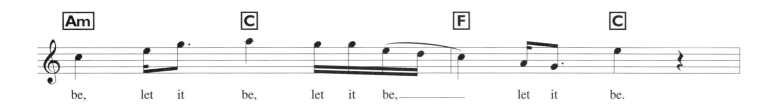

be, let it be, let it be, let it be.

Whis - per words of wis - dom, let it be.___ And

when the bro - ken heart - ed peo - ple liv - ing in the world a - gree,

there will be an ans - wer, let it be.___ Let it

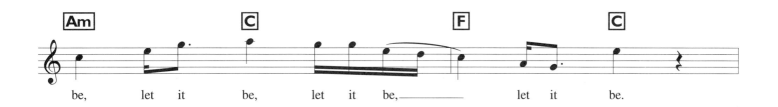

be, let it be, let it be,___ let it be.

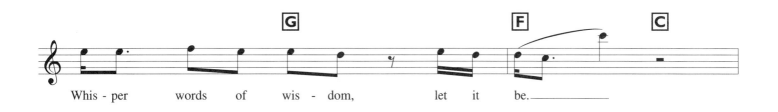

Whis - per words of wis - dom, let it be.___

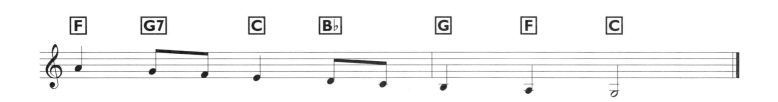

LET'S TWIST AGAIN

Words & Music by Kal Mann & Dave Appell

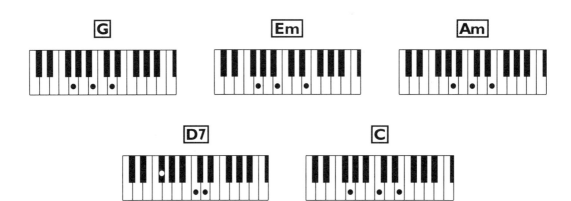

Voice: **Electric Piano 2**

Rhythm: **Twist**

Tempo: ♩ = **140**

Let's twist a - gain_____ like we did last

sum - mer,_____ yeah, let's twist a - gain,_____

like we did last year._____ Do you re -

- mem - ber when_____ things were real - ly hum - ming,_____

THE LOCO-MOTION

Words & Music by Gerry Goffin & Carole King
© Copyright 1962 Screen Gems-Columbia Music Incorporated, USA.
Screen Gems-EMI Music Limited.
All Rights Reserved. International Copyright Secured.
.

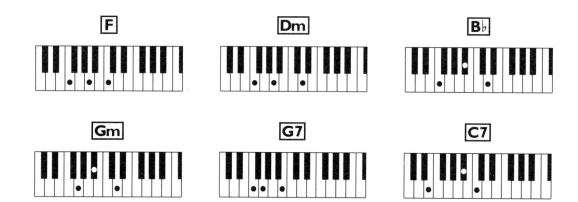

Voice: **Piano**

Rhythm: **4 Beat Rock**

Tempo: ♩ = 124

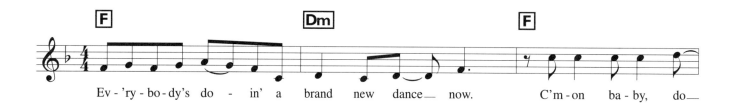

Ev-'ry-bo-dy's do-in' a brand new dance— now. C'm-on ba-by, do—

—— the lo-co-mo-tion. I know you'll get to like it if you give it a chance— now.

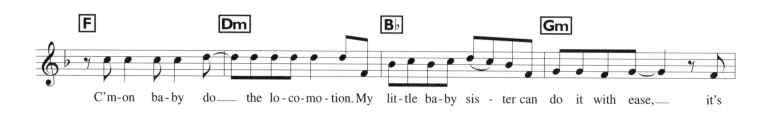

C'm-on ba-by do— the lo-co-mo-tion. My lit-tle ba-by sis-ter can do it with ease,— it's

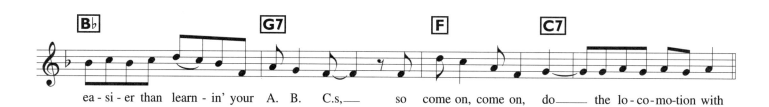

ea-si-er than learn-in' your A. B. C.s,— so come on, come on, do— the lo-co-mo-tion with

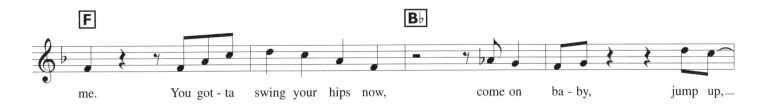

me. You got-ta swing your hips now, come on ba-by, jump up,—

— jump back,— oh well I think you got the knack.

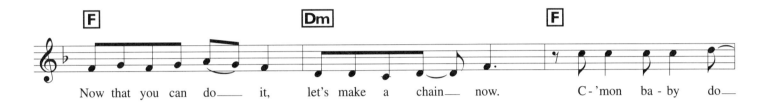

Now that you can do— it, let's make a chain— now. C-'mon ba-by do—

— the lo-co-mo-tion. A chug-a chug-a mo-tion like a rail-road train— now.

C'm-on ba-by do— the lo-co-mo-tion. Do it nice and ea-sy now,— don't lose con-trol,— a

lit-tle bit of rhy-thm and a lot of soul.— Come on, come on, do— the lo-co-mo-tion with

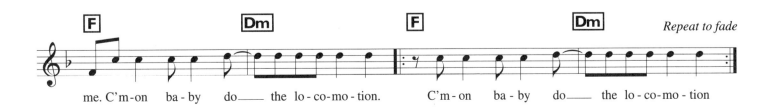

Repeat to fade

me. C'm-on ba-by do— the lo-co-mo-tion. C'm-on ba-by do— the lo-co-mo-tion

MAH NA MAH NA

Words & Music by Piero Umiliani

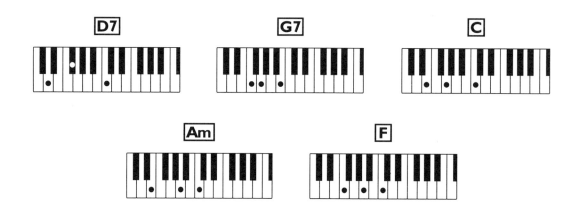

Voice: **Brass/Strings Layer**

Rhythm: **Big Band**

Tempo: ♩ = 150

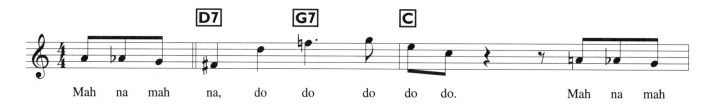

Mah na mah na, do do do do do. Mah na mah

na, do do do do.___ Mah na mah na, do do do

do do, do do do, do do do, do do do do do do do do do do.

Mah na mah na mah na mah mah na na mah___ mah de

di de uh uh. Mah na mah na___ mah na na mah mah.

Da da da da___ da. Da da da da

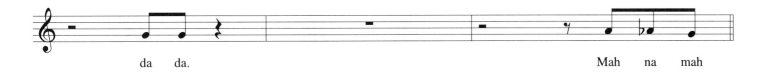

da da. Mah na mah

na, do do do do do. Mah na mah na, do do do do.___

___ Mah na mah na, do do do do do, do do do, do

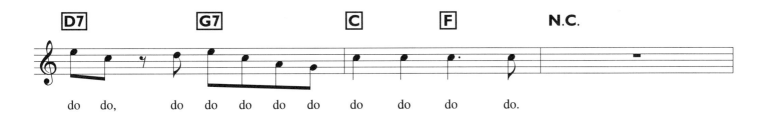

do do, do do do do do do do do do.

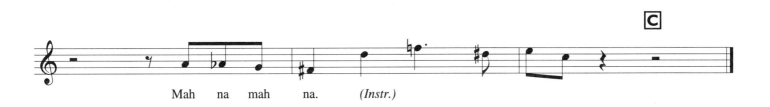

Mah na mah na. *(Instr.)*

MRS ROBINSON

Words & Music by Paul Simon

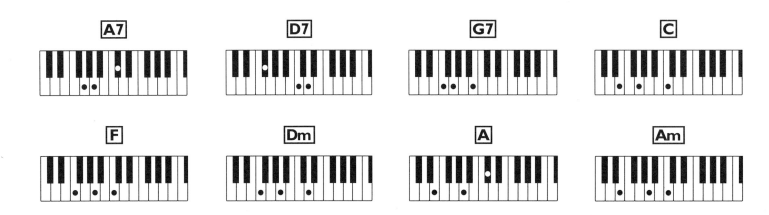

Voice: **Accordian**

Rhythm: **Soft Rock**

Tempo: ♩ = 112

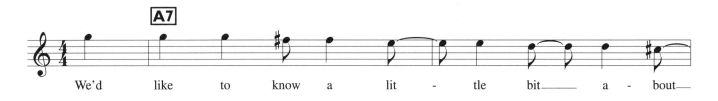

We'd like to know a lit - tle bit__ a - bout__

__ you for our files.__ We'd like to help you

learn to help your - self.__ Look a - round you, all

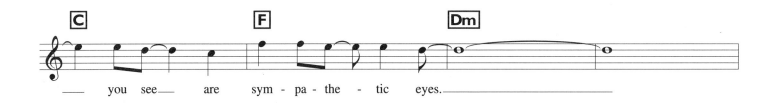

__ you see__ are sym - pa - the - tic eyes.__

A — Stroll a - round the grounds un - til you feel at home. **G7**

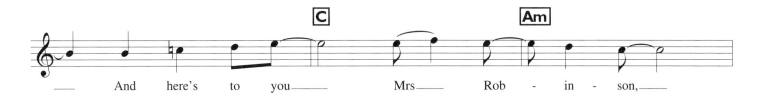

And here's to you Mrs Rob - in - son, **C** **Am**

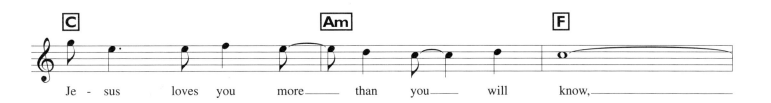

C Je - sus loves you more than you will know, **Am** **F**

G7 (wo wo wo.) God bless you

C please Mrs Rob - in - son, **Am** hea - ven holds a place **C**

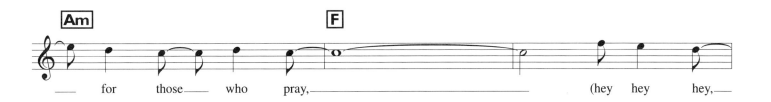

Am for those who pray, **F** (hey hey hey,

Dm hey hey hey. **A**)

NIGHT FEVER

Words & Music by Barry Gibb, Maurice Gibb & Robin Gibb

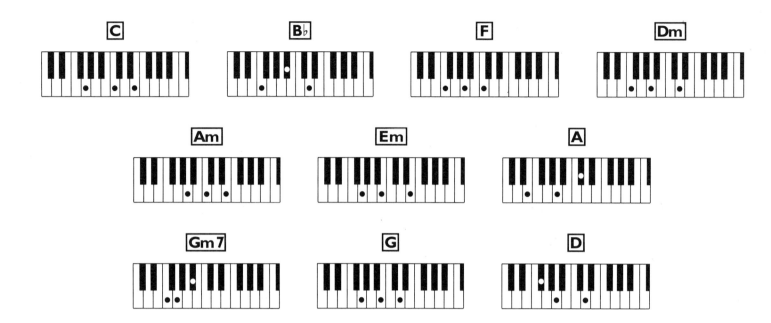

Voice: **String/Piano Split**

Rhythm: **Pop Rock 1**

Tempo: ♩ = 120

Lis-ten to— the ground, there is move-ment all— a-round, there is some-thing go - ing down and I can

feel it. On the waves of— the air, there is danc - ing out— there,— if it's

some-thing we can share, we can steal it. And that sweet ci - ty wo - man, she

moves through the light,___ con-troll-ing my mind_ and my soul.___ When you reach out for me,_ yeah, and the

feel-ing is___ bright.__Then I get night fe-ver, night fe-ver,___ we know how to do it.

Gim-me that night fe-ver, night fe-ver,___ we know how to show it.

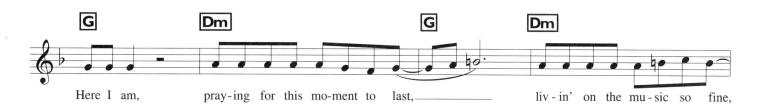

Here I am, pray-ing for this mo-ment to last,_____ liv-in' on the mu-sic so fine,

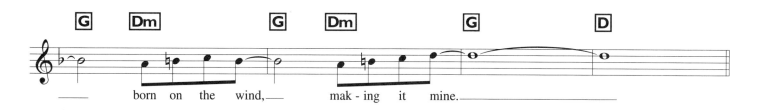

___ born on the wind,___ mak-ing it mine.

Night fe-ver, night fe-ver,___ we know how to do it. Gim-me that

Repeat to fade

night fe-ver, night fe-ver,___ we know how to show it.

NO REGRETS

Words & Music by Robbie Williams & Guy Chambers

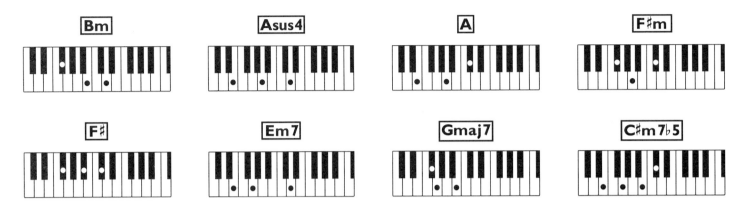

Voice: **Acoustic Guitar**

Rhythm: **Lite Pop**

Tempo: ♩ = 104

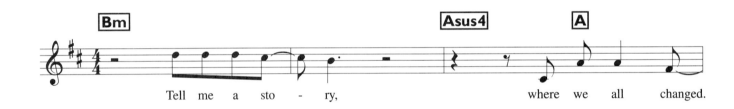

Tell me a sto - ry, where we all changed.

And we'd live our lives to - geth - er

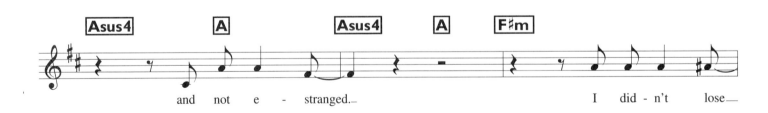

and not e - stranged.___ I did - n't lose___

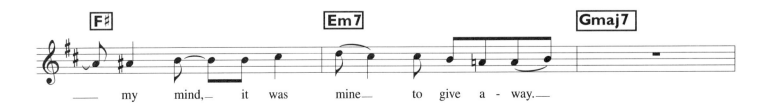

___ my mind,___ it was mine___ to give a - way.___

Could-n't stay to watch___ me cry,___ you did-n't have the time,___ so I

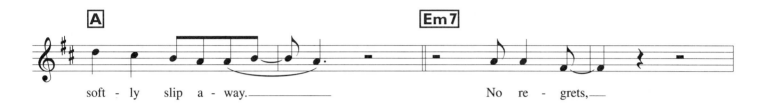

soft - ly slip a - way.___ No re - grets,___

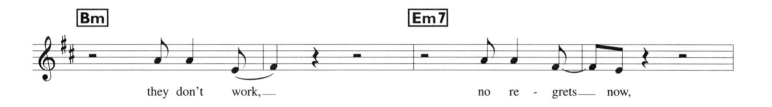

they don't work,___ no re - grets___ now,

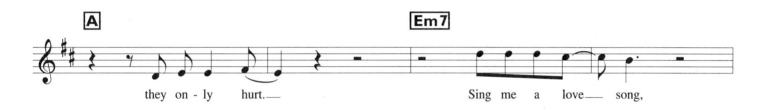

they on - ly hurt.___ Sing me a love___ song,

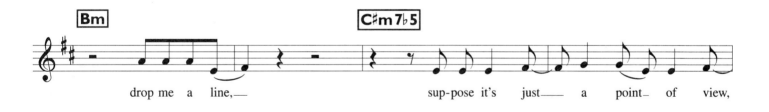

drop me a line,___ sup-pose it's just___ a point__ of view,

___ but they tell___ me I'm do - ing fine.___

OLIVER'S ARMY

Words & Music by Elvis Costello

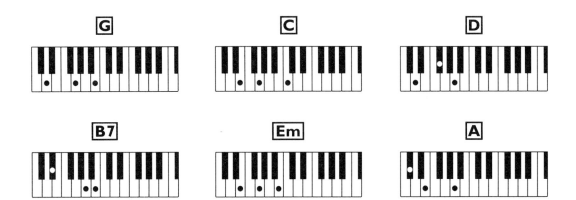

Voice: **Piano**

Rhythm: **Soft Rock 2**

Tempo: ♩ = **136**

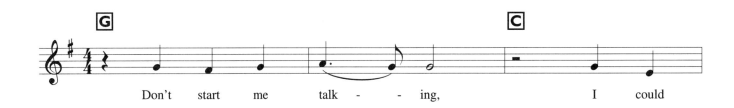

Don't start me talk - - ing, I could

talk all night._____ My mind goes sleep walk - ing

while I'm put - ting the world___ to right. Called car - eers___

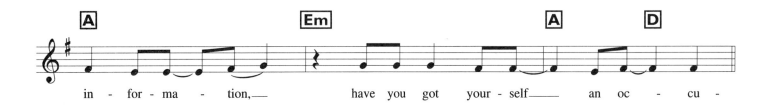

in - for - ma - tion,___ have you got your - self___ an oc - cu -

Oliver's ar - - - my is here to stay, _____
- pa - - - tion.

Oliver's ar - my are on their way, _____ and I would

ra - ther be a - ny - where else but _____ here to - - -

- day.   And I would ra - ther be a - ny - where

else but _____ here to - - day.   And I would

ra - ther be a - ny - where else but _____ here to - -

Repeat to fade

Oh, _____   oh, oh, oh.   Oh, _____   oh, oh, oh. _____
- day. _____

RELEASE ME

Words & Music by Eddie Miller, Dub Williams & Robert Yount

Voice: **Clarinet**

Rhythm: **Soft Rock**

Tempo: ♩ = 110

- gain.   Please,   re - lease me, can't you

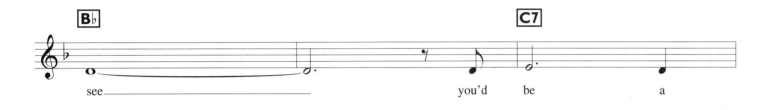

see   you'd be   a

fool to   cling   to   me.   To

live   a   lie would bring us pain,

so   re - lease me   and   let me love a -

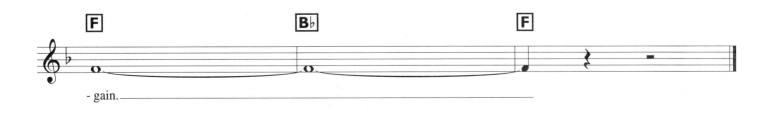

- gain.

RIDERS ON THE STORM

Words & Music by Jim Morrison, Robbie Krieger, Ray Manzarek & John Densmore

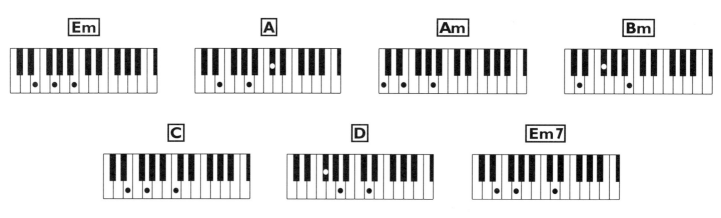

Voice: **Electric Guitar**

Rhythm: **8 Beat Pop**

Tempo: ♩ = 120

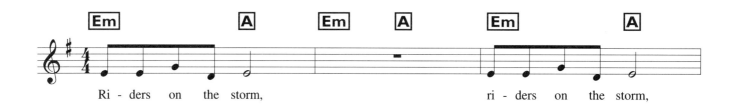

Ri - ders on the storm, ri - ders on the storm,

in - to this house we're born, in -

-to this world we're thrown. Like a dog with out a bone, an

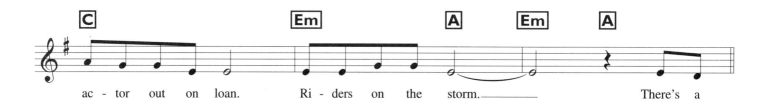

ac - tor out on loan. Ri - ders on the storm. There's a

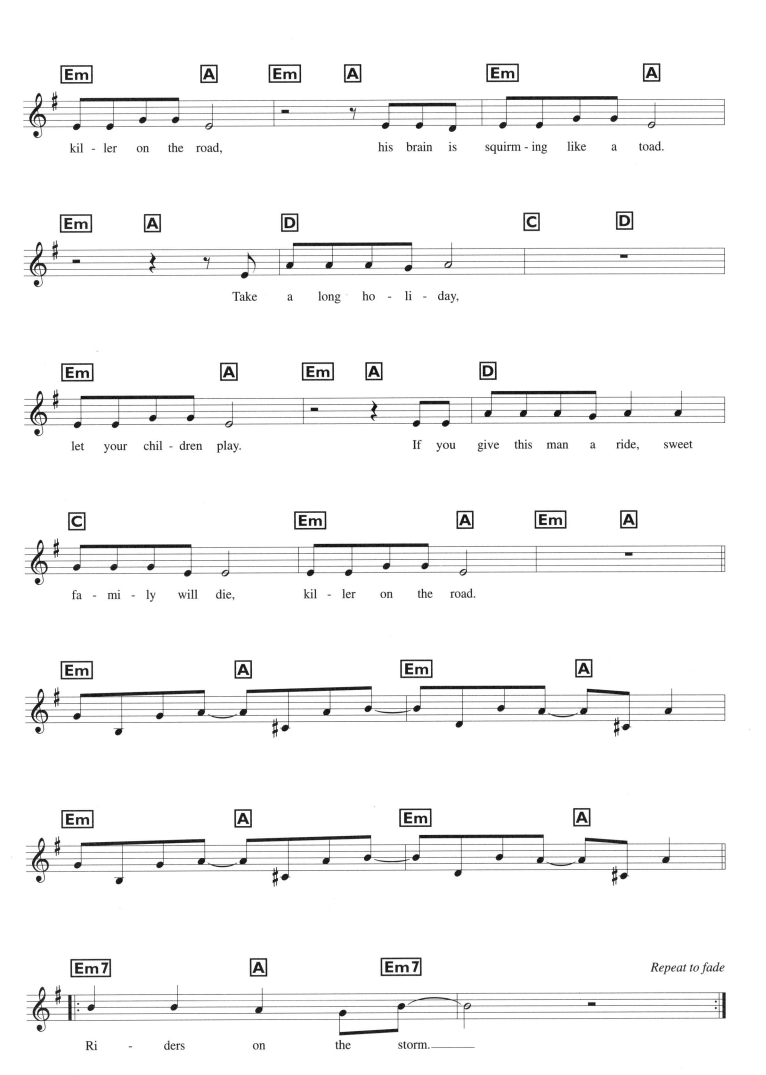

ROCKIN' ALL OVER THE WORLD

Words & Music by John Fogerty
© Copyright 1975 Wenaha Music Company, USA.
Hornall Brothers Music Limited.
All Rights Reserved. International Copyright Secured.

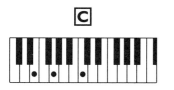 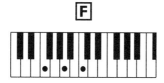 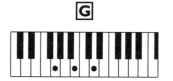 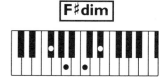

Voice: **Distortion Guitar**

Rhythm: **4 Beat Rock**

Tempo: ♩ = 132

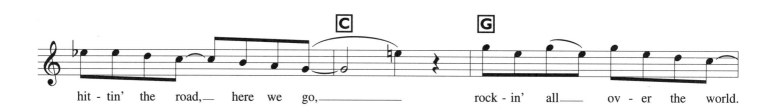

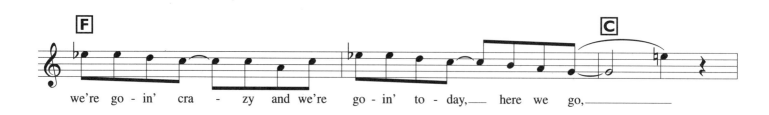

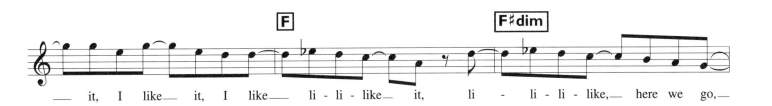

it, I like it, I like li - li - like it, li - li - li - like, here we go,

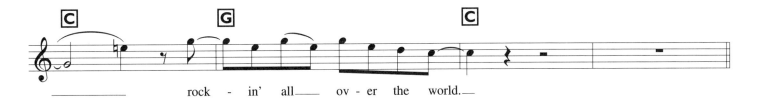

rock - in' all ov - er the world.

Gon - na tell your ma - ma what you're gon - na do, so come on out with your

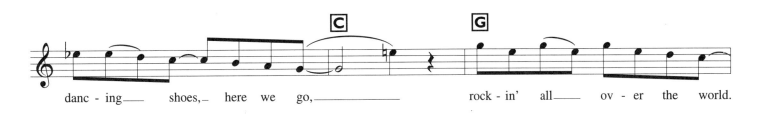

danc - ing shoes, here we go, rock - in' all ov - er the world.

And I like it, I like it, I like

it, I like it, I li - li - li - like it, li - li - li - like, here we go,

Repeat to fade

rock - in' all ov - er the world. Well I like

SACRIFICE

Words & Music by Elton John & Bernie Taupin
© Copyright 1989 Big Pig Music Limited.
Warner/Chappell Music Limited.
All Rights Reserved. International Copyright Secured.

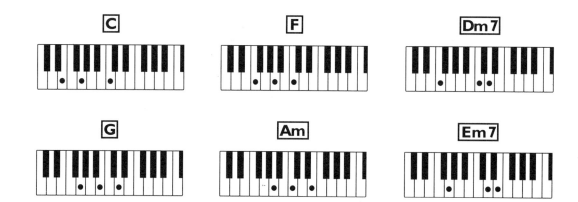

Voice: **Studio Piano**

Rhythm: **Soft Rock 2**

Tempo: ♩ = 116

It's a hu-man sign___ when things___ go___ wrong,___

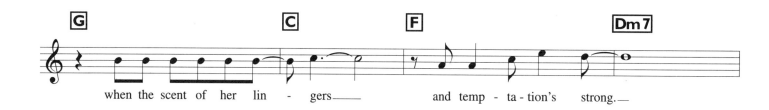

when the scent of her lin - gers___ and temp - ta-tion's strong.___

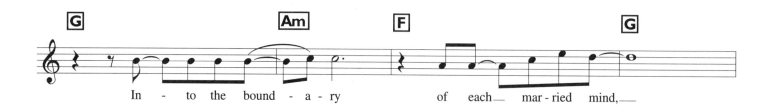

In - to the bound - a - ry of each___ mar - ried mind,___

sweet de - ceit comes a - call - ing___ and ne - ga - ti - vi - ty lands.___

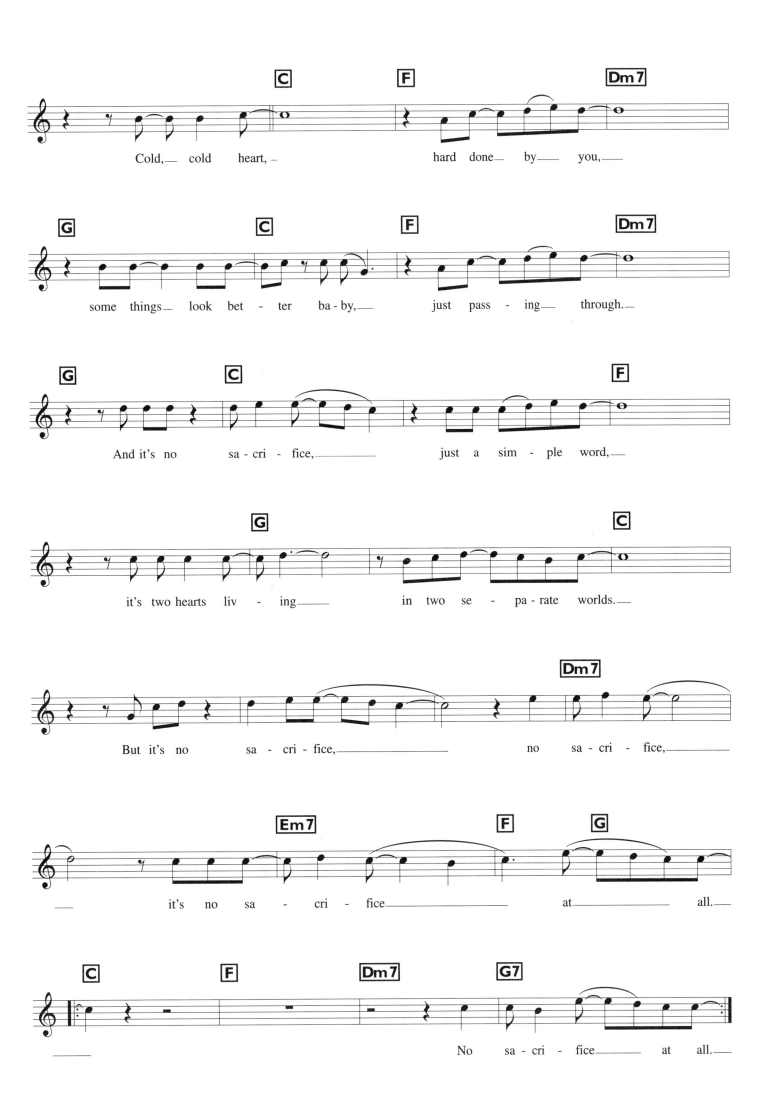

SAN FRANCISCO
(Be Sure To Wear Some Flowers In Your Hair)

Words & Music by John Phillips

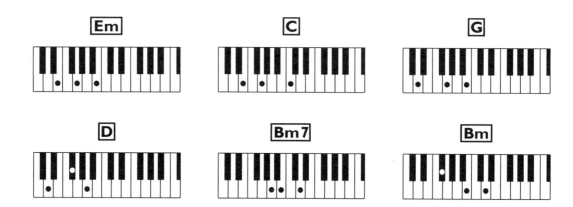

Voice: **Flute**

Rhythm: **Pop Ballad**

Tempo: ♩ = 120

If you're go-ing to San Fran -

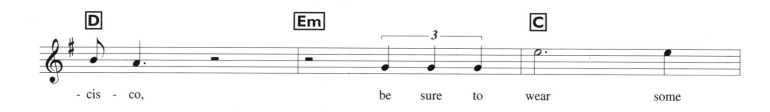

- cis - co, be sure to wear some

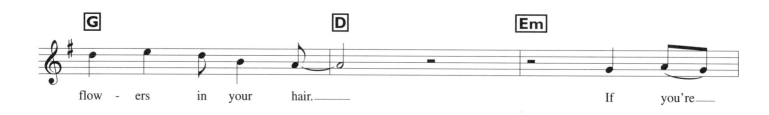

flow - ers in your hair. If you're

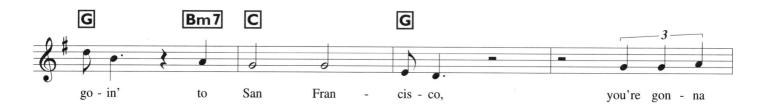

go - in' to San Fran - cis - co, you're gon - na

meet   some   gen - tle   peo - ple   there.

For   those   who   come   to   San   Fran - - -

- cis - co,   sum - mer   time   will

be   a   love - in   there.   In   the

streets   of   San   Fran - - - cis - co,

gen - tle   peo - ple   with   flow - ers   in   their

hair.

SOMETHING IN THE AIR

Words & Music by John Keen

F | C7sus4

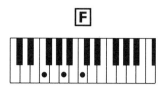 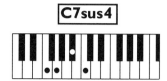

Voice: **Brass Ensemble**

Rhythm: **Straight Rock**

Tempo: ♩ = 90

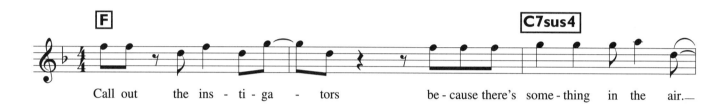

Call out the ins - ti - ga - tors because there's some - thing in the air.

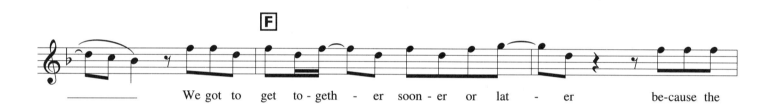

We got to get to - geth - er soon - er or lat - er be - cause the

re - vo - lu - tion's here and you know it's right,

and you know that it's right.

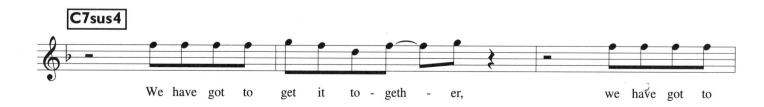

We have got to get it to - geth - er, we have got to

get it to - geth - er now.____

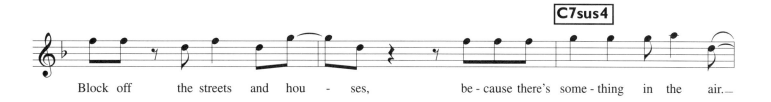

Block off the streets and hou - ses, be - cause there's some - thing in the air.____

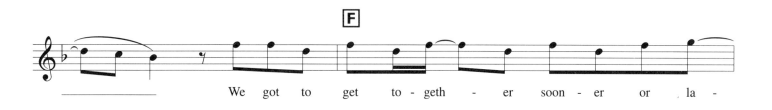

____ We got to get to - geth - er soon - er or la -

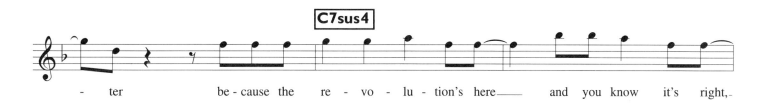

- ter be - cause the re - vo - lu - tion's here____ and you know it's right,-

____ and you know that____ it's

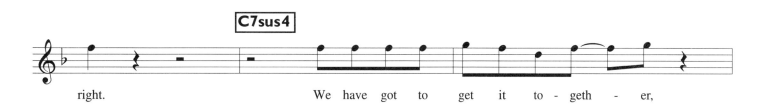

right. We have got to get it to - geth - er,

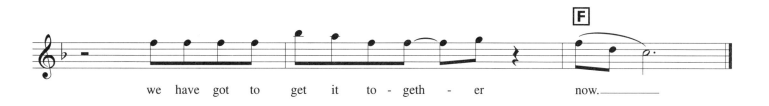

we have got to get it to - geth - er now.____

SPIRIT IN THE SKY

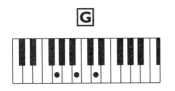 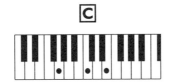 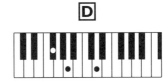 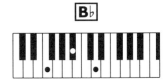

Voice: **Electric Guitar**

Rhythm: **Chicago Blues**

Tempo: ♩ = 138

When I die and they lay me to rest,

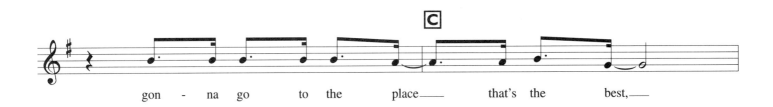

gon - na go to the place that's the best,

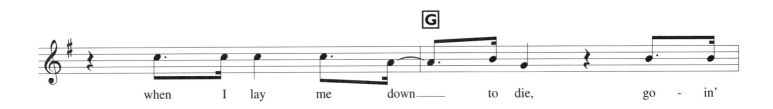

when I lay me down to die, go - in'

up to the spi - - rit in the sky.

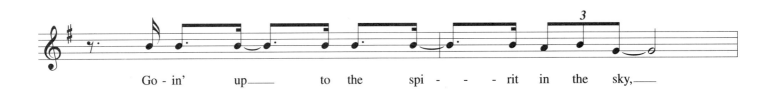

Go - in' up to the spi - - rit in the sky,

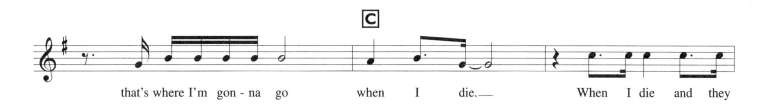

that's where I'm gon - na go   when I die.——   When I die and they

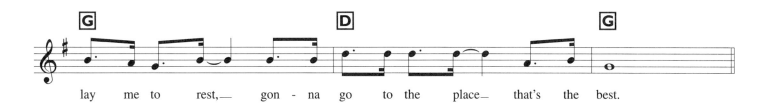

lay me to rest,——   gon - na go to the place—— that's the best.

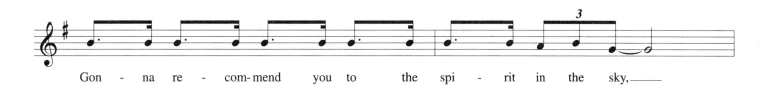

Gon - na re - com- mend you to the spi - rit in the sky,————

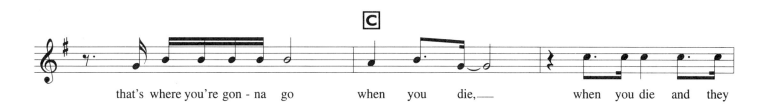

that's where you're gon - na go   when you die,——   when you die and they

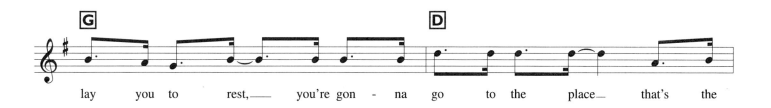

lay you to rest,——   you're gon - na go to the place—— that's the

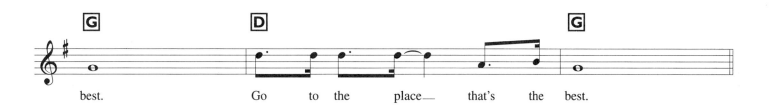

best.   Go to the place—— that's the best.

Repeat to fade

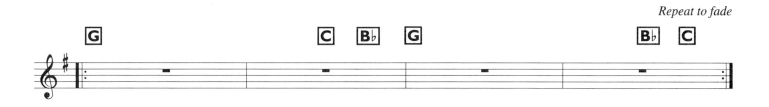

THINK TWICE

Words & Music by Andy Hill & Pete Sinfield

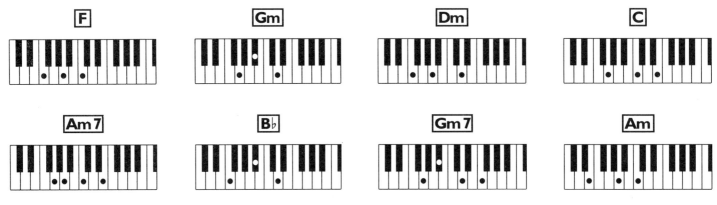

Voice: **Electric Guitar**

Rhythm: **Pop Rock 1**

Tempo: ♩ = 128

Don't think I can't feel that there's some - thing wrong._____

You've been the sweet - est part of____ my life____ for so____ long.

I look in your eyes there's a dis - tant light,_____

and you and I know_____ there'll be a storm to - night.____

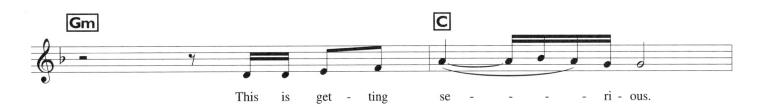

This is get - ting se - - - - ri - ous.

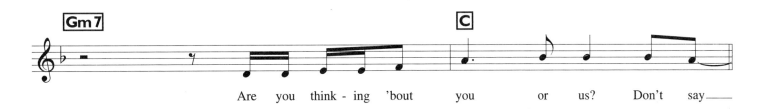

Are you think - ing 'bout you or us? Don't say____

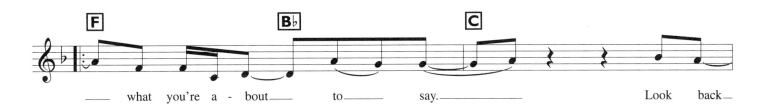

____ what you're a - bout____ to____ say._____ Look back____

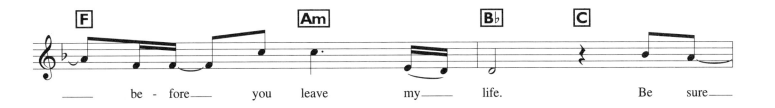

____ be - fore____ you leave my____ life. Be sure____

____ be - fore____ you close that door,_____ be - fore you roll____

Repeat ad lib. to fade

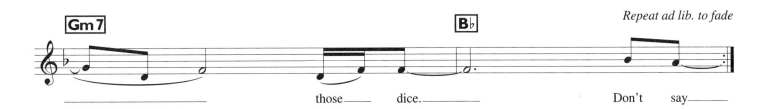

those____ dice.____ Don't say____

TILL THERE WAS YOU

Words & Music by Meredith Willson
© Copyright 1950, 1954 & 1957 Frank Music Corporation, USA.
© Copyright renewed 1978, 1982 Frank Music Corporation/Meredith Willson Music.
MPL Communications Limited.
All Rights Reserved. International Copyright Secured.

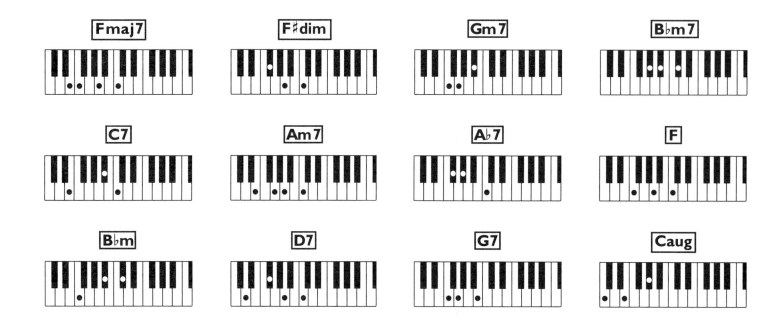

Voice: **Jazz Organ**

Rhythm: **Ballad**

Tempo: ♩ = 92

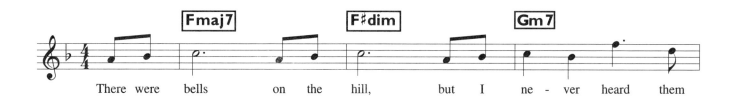

There were bells on the hill, but I ne - ver heard them

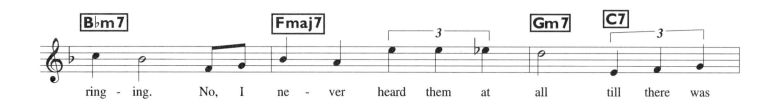

ring - ing. No, I ne - ver heard them at all till there was

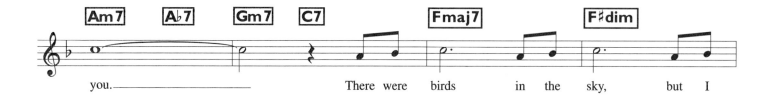

you.＿＿＿＿＿ There were birds in the sky, but I

ne - ver saw them wing - ing. No, I ne - ver saw them at

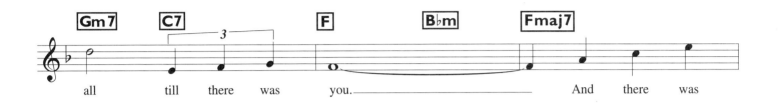

all till there was you._____ And there was

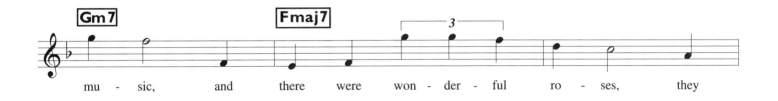

mu - sic, and there were won - der - ful ro - ses, they

tell me in sweet fra - grant mea - dows of

dawn and dew. There was love all a -

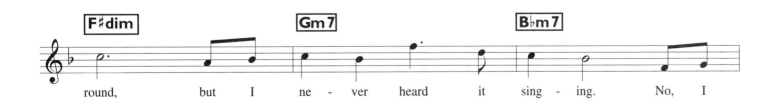

round, but I ne - ver heard it sing - ing. No, I

ne - ver heard it at all till there was you._____

TRAGEDY

Words & Music by Barry Gibb, Maurice Gibb & Robin Gibb

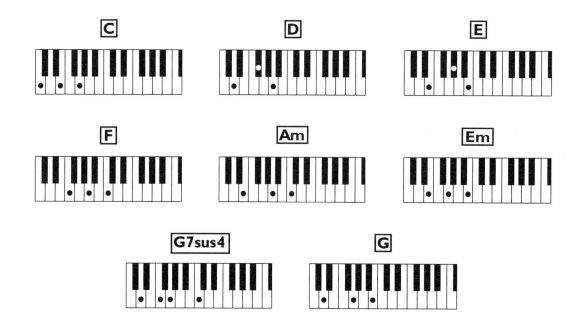

Voice: **Brass I**

Rhythm: **8 Beat Pop**

Tempo: ♩ **= 98**

Here I lie in a lost and lone-ly part of town. Held in time, in a

world of tears I slow-ly drown. Go-in' home, I just can't make it

all a-lone, I real-ly should be hold-ing you, hold-ing you, lov-ing you,

lov - ing you.___ Tra - ge - dy,___ when the feel - ing's gone and you can't go on, it's

tra - ge - dy.___ When the morn - ing cries and you don't know why, it's hard to___ bear,___ with

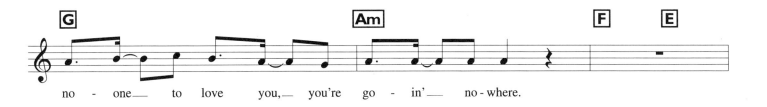

no - one___ to love you,___ you're go - in'___ no - where.

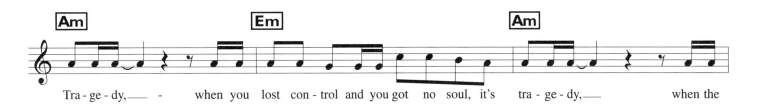

Tra - ge - dy,___ - when you lost con - trol and you got no soul, it's tra - ge - dy,___ when the

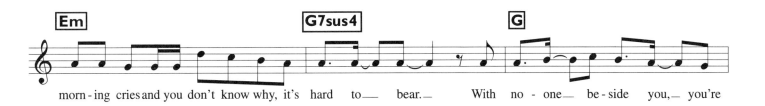

morn - ing cries and you don't know why, it's hard to___ bear.___ With no - one___ be - side you,___ you're

go - in'___ no - where.

Ah!

TRY A LITTLE TENDERNESS

Words & Music by Harry Woods, Jimmy Campbell & Reg Connelly

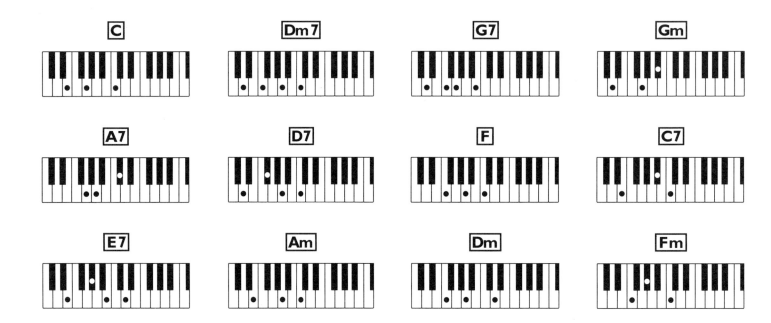

Voice: **Clarinet**

Rhythm: **2 Beat**

Tempo: ♩ = **96**

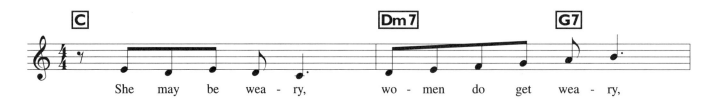

She may be wea - ry, wo - men do get wea - ry,

wear - ing the same shab - by dress. And when she's wea - ry,

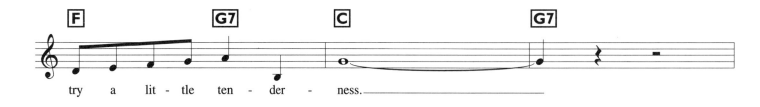

try a lit - tle ten - der - ness.

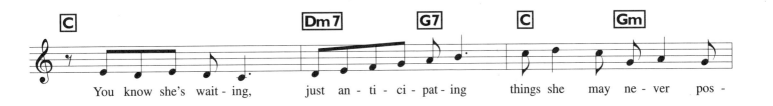

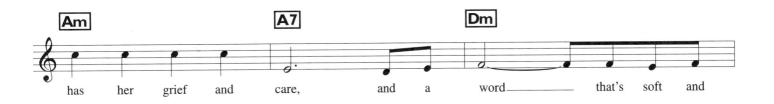

UPTOWN GIRL

Words & Music by Billy Joel
© Copyright 1983 Joelsongs, USA.
EMI Songs Limited.
All Rights Reserved. International Copyright Secured.

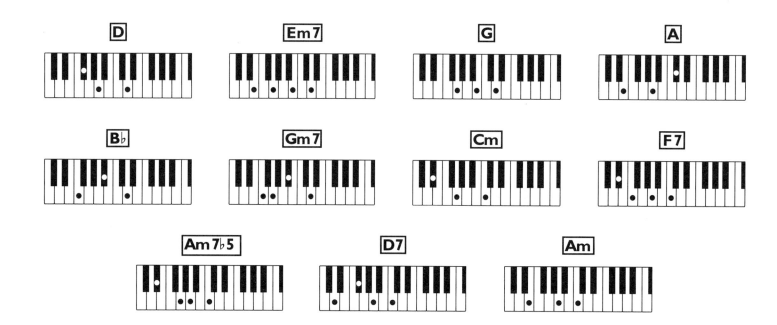

Voice: **Saxophone**

Rhythm: **Steady Rock**

Tempo: ♩ = 124

Oh._____ Oh._____

Up - town girl, she's been liv - ing in her up - town___ world.

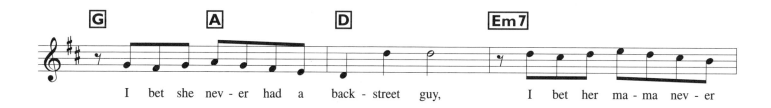

I bet she nev - er had a back - street guy, I bet her ma - ma nev - er

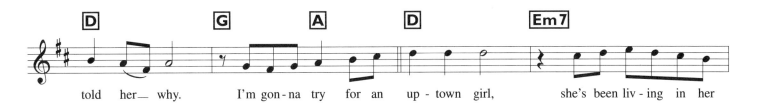

told her— why.　I'm gon-na try　for an up-town girl,　she's been liv-ing in her

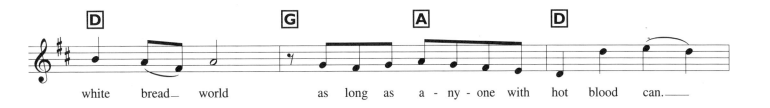

white bread— world　as long as a-ny-one with hot blood can.——

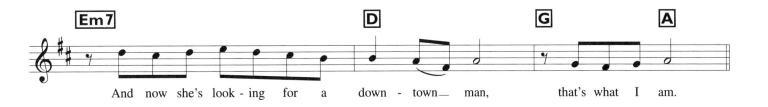

And now she's look-ing for a down-town— man,　that's what I am.

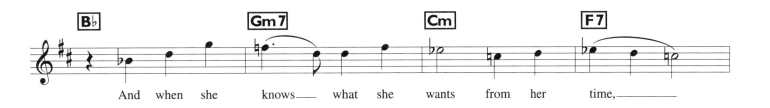

And when she knows— what she wants from her time,————

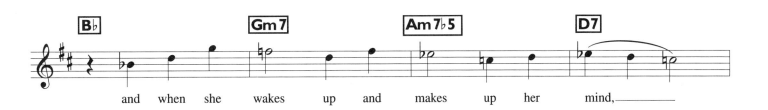

and when she wakes up and makes up her mind,————

she'll see I'm not so tough just be-cause I'm in love with an

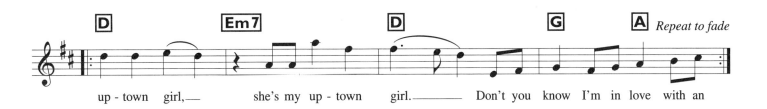

up-town girl,—　she's my up-town girl.——— Don't you know I'm in love with an

WE ARE FAMILY

Words & Music by Bernard Edwards & Nile Rodgers
© Copyright 1979 Bernard's Other Music/Sony/ATV Songs LLC, USA.
Warner/Chappell Music Limited / Sony/ATV Music Publishing (UK) Limited.
All Rights Reserved. International Copyright Secured.

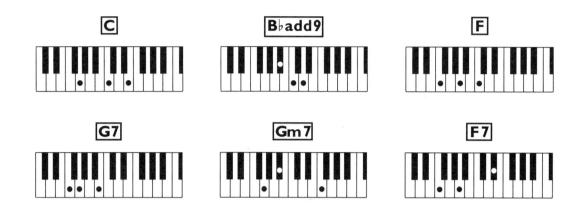

Voice: **Electric Piano**

Rhythm: **Funk**

Tempo: ♩ = 118

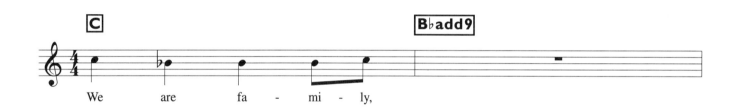

We are fa - mi - ly,

I got all my sis - ters with me.   We are fa - mi - ly,

get up ev - 'ry - bo - dy and sing.

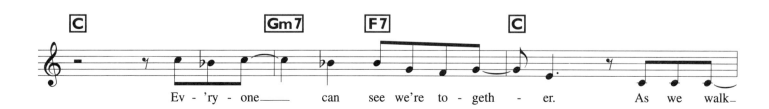

Ev - 'ry - one can see we're to - geth - er.   As we walk

A WHOLE NEW WORLD
(From Walt Disney Pictures' "Aladdin")

Words by Tim Rice
Music by Alan Menken

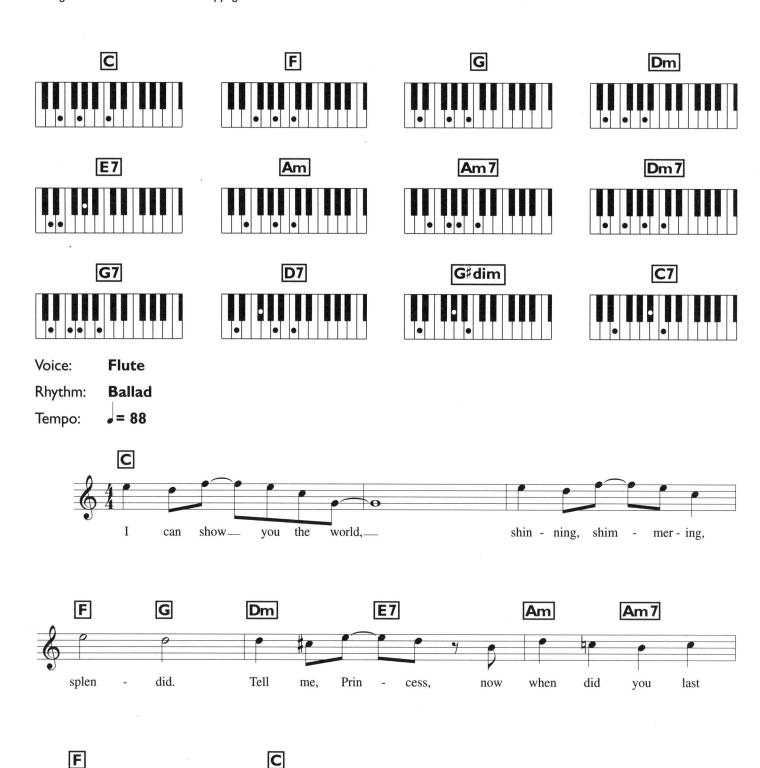

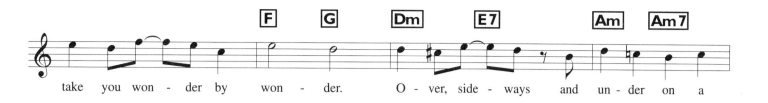

take you won - der by won - der. O - ver, side - ways and un - der on a

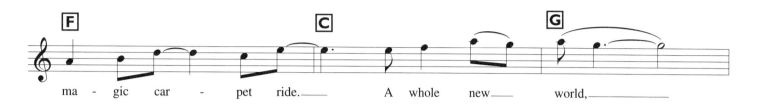

ma - gic car - pet ride._____ A whole new_____ world,_____

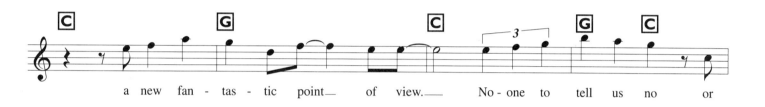

a new fan - tas - tic point_____ of view._____ No - one to tell us no or

where to go_____ or say we're on - ly_____ dream - ing. A whole new world,

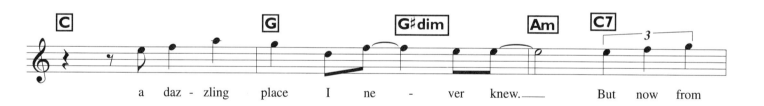

a daz - zling place I ne - ver knew._____ But now from

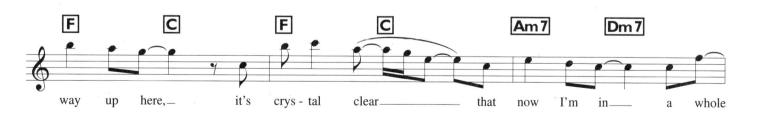

way up here,_____ it's crys - tal clear_____ that now I'm in_____ a whole

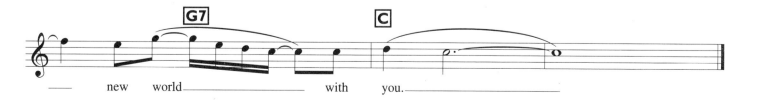

_____ new world_____ with you._____

WILD WOOD

Words & Music by Paul Weller

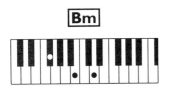 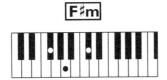 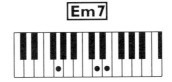 

Voice: **Alto Saxophone**

Rhythm: **Soft Rock**

Tempo: ♩ = 154

High tide, mid af - ter - noon,

peo -

- ple fly by in the

traf - fic's boom.

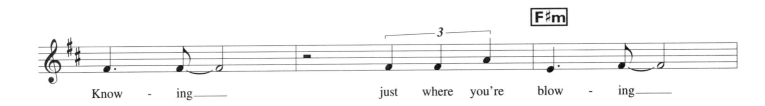

Know - ing just where you're blow - ing

get - ting to where_____ you_____ should be

go - - - ing._____ And I say

climb - ing for - ev - er_____

_____ try - - - ing, you're gon - na find your way out

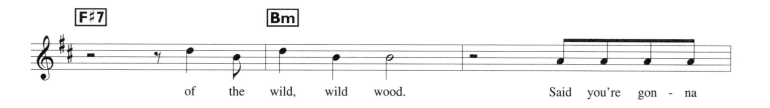

of the wild, wild wood. Said you're gon - na

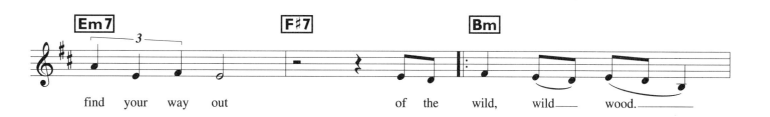

find your way out of the wild, wild_____ wood._____

Repeat to fade

Of the

THE WIND BENEATH MY WINGS

Words & Music by Jeff Silbar & Larry Henley

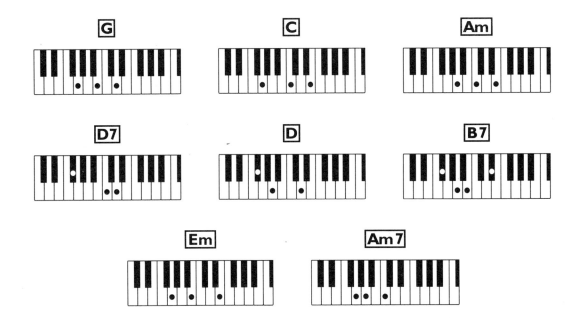

Voice: **Jazz Organ**

Rhythm: **16 Beat**

Tempo: ♩ = **104**

It must have been cold___ there___ in my sha - dow,

to ne - ver have sun - light___ on your face.

You've been con - tent___ to let me shine,

you al - ways walked___ the step be - hind.___

Did you ev - er know___ that you're my___ he - ro,

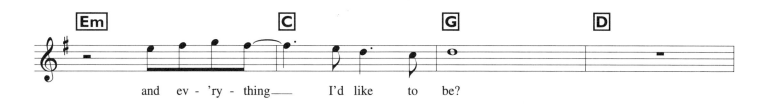

and ev - 'ry - thing___ I'd like to be?

I can fly high - - - er than an ea - - - - -

- gle,___ 'cause you are the wind___ be - neath my

wings. You are the wind___ be - neath my___

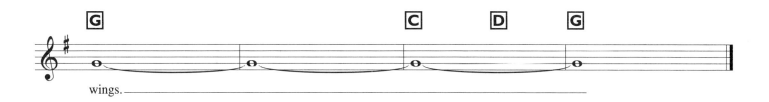

wings.___

WITH A LITTLE HELP FROM MY FRIENDS

Words & Music by John Lennon & Paul McCartney
© Copyright 1967 Northern Songs.
All Rights Reserved. International Copyright Secured.

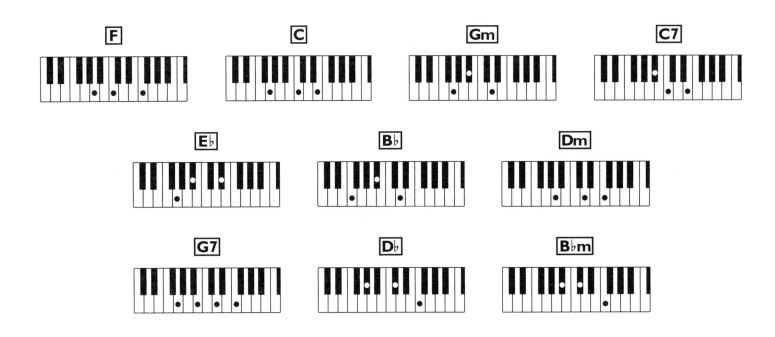

Voice: **Clarinet**

Rhythm: **2 Beat**

Tempo: ♩ = 120

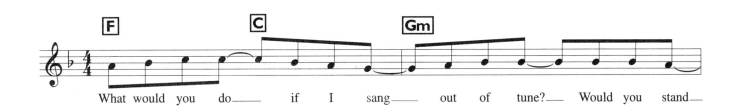

What would you do___ if I sang___ out of tune?___ Would you stand___

___ up and walk___ out on me?___ Lend me your ears___ and I'll sing___

___ you a song___ and I'll try___ not to sing___ out of key.___ Oh, I get by___

_____ with a lit-tle help_ from my friends.__ Mm, I get high_ with a lit-tle help_ from my friends.

_____ Mm, I'm gon-na try_ with a lit-tle help_ from my friends._ (Do you need_ a-ny-bo-

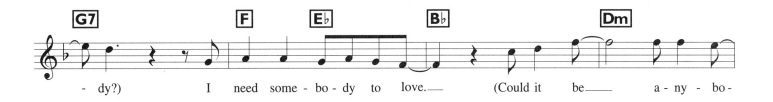

- dy?) I need some-bo-dy to love._ (Could it be_ a-ny-bo-

- dy?) I want some-bo-dy to love._ Oh, I get by_ with a lit-tle help_ from my friends.

_____ Mm, I'm gon-na try_ with a lit-tle help_ from my friends._ Oh I get high_

_____ with a lit-tle help_ from my friends._ Yes I' get by_ with a lit-tle help_ from my friends,

_____ with a lit-tle help_ from my friends._____

A WOMAN IN LOVE

Words & Music by Barry Gibb & Robin Gibb

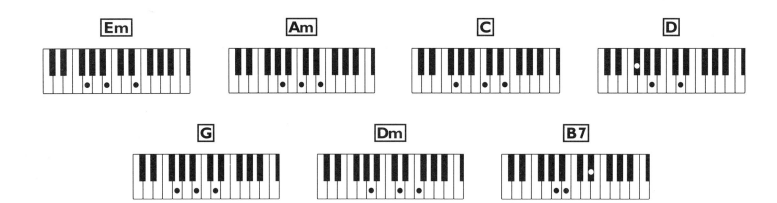

Voice: **Piano 2**

Rhythm: **Pop Ballad**

Tempo: ♩ = 100

Life is a mo-ment in space,___ when the dream is gone,___ it's a lone-li-er place,

___ I kiss the morn-ing good-bye,___ but down in-side___

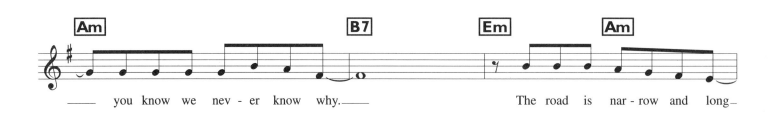

___ you know we nev-er know why.___ The road is nar-row and long___

___ when eyes meet eyes___ and the feel-ing is strong.___

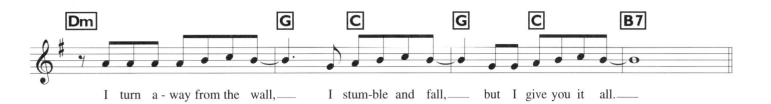

I turn a-way from the wall,___ I stum-ble and fall,___ but I give you it all.___

I am a wo-man in love___ and I'd do a-ny-thing___ to get you in-to my world,

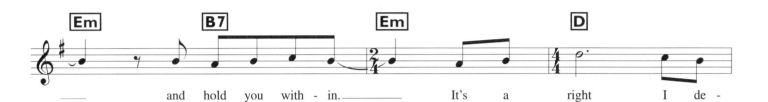

___ and hold you with - in.___ It's a right I de -

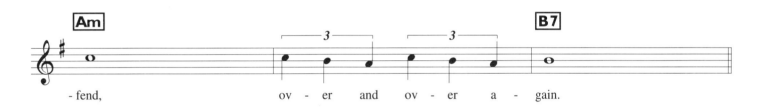

- fend, ov - er and ov - er a - gain.

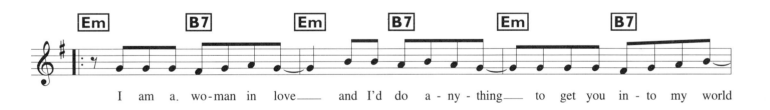

I am a. wo-man in love___ and I'd do a-ny-thing___ to get you in-to my world

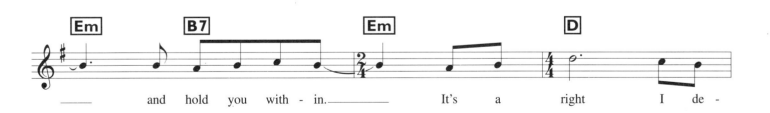

___ and hold you with - in.___ It's a right I de -

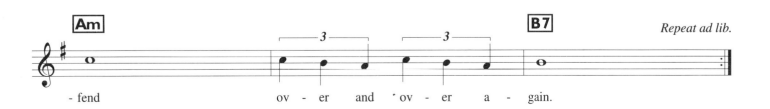

- fend ov - er and ov - er a - gain.

Y.M.C.A.

Words & Music by Jacques Morali, Henri Belolo & Victor Willis
© Copyright 1978 Scorpio Music, France.
EMI Music Publishing Limited.
All Rights Reserved. International Copyright Secured.

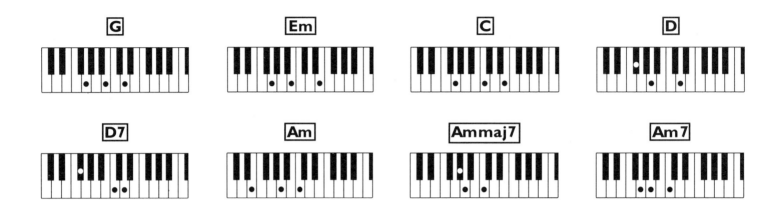

Voice: **Electric Guitar**

Rhythm: **Pop Rock 1**

Tempo: ♩ = **128**

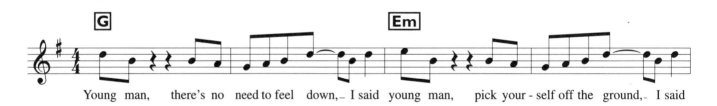

Young man, there's no need to feel down,— I said young man, pick your-self off the ground,— I said

young man, 'cause you're in a new town,— there's no need to— be— un-hap-py.

Young man, there's a place you can go,— I said young man, when you're

short on your dough,— you can stay there, and I'm sure you will find— ma-ny

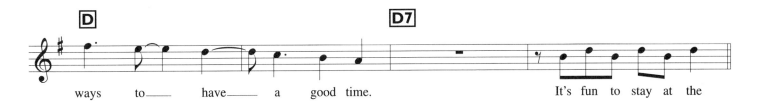

ways to—— have—— a good time.
It's fun to stay at the

Y. M. C. A.,——— it's fun to stay at the——— Y. M. C. A.———

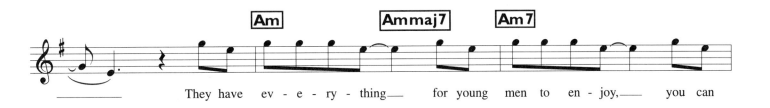

——————— They have ev - e - ry - thing—— for young men to en - joy,——— you can

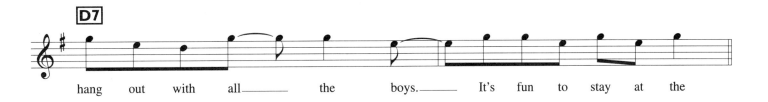

hang out with all——— the boys.——— It's fun to stay at the

Y. M. C. A.,——— it's fun to stay at the

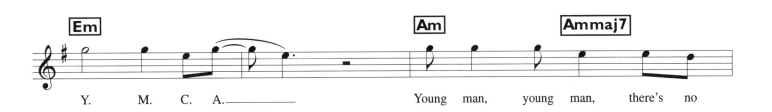

Y. M. C. A.——————— Young man, young man, there's no

Repeat to fade

need to feel down,——— young man, young man, pick your - self off the ground..

YOU'LL NEVER WALK ALONE

Words & Music by Richard Rodgers
Words by Oscar Hammerstein II

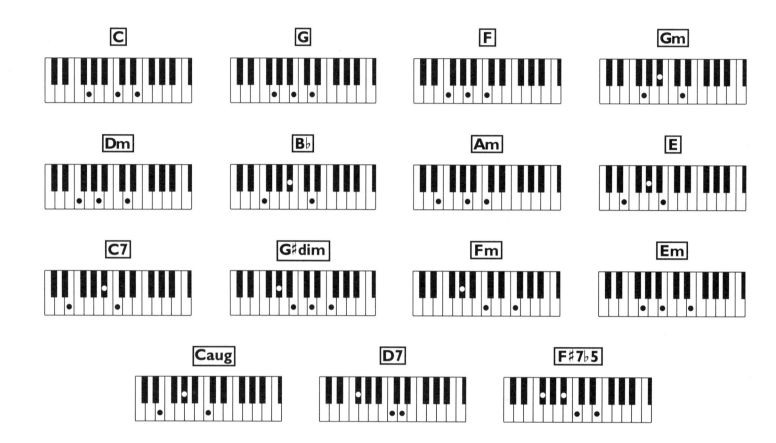

Voice: **String/Piano**

Rhythm: **Love Ballad**

Tempo: ♩· = **92**

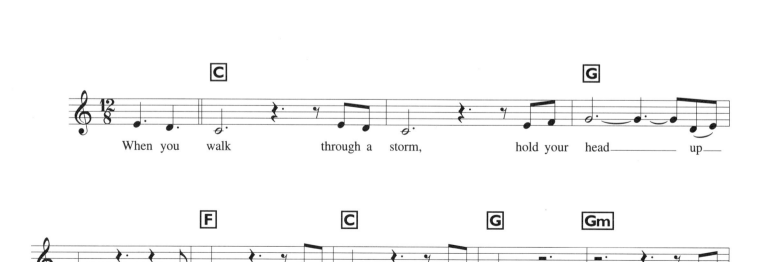

When you walk through a storm, hold your head_____ up_____

high and don't be a-fraid of the dark. At the

YOU'RE MY BEST FRIEND

Words & Music by John Deacon
© Copyright 1975 Trident Music/B. Feldman & Company Limited.
All Rights Reserved. International Copyright Secured.

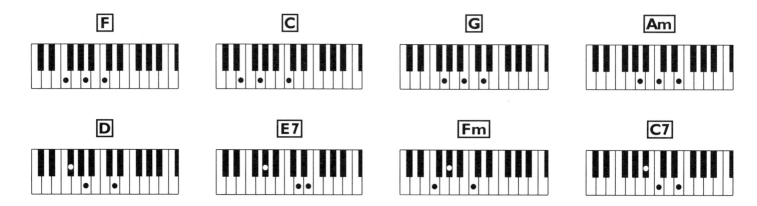

Voice: **Soprano Saxophone**

Rhythm: **Slow Rock 2**

Tempo: ♩ = 120

Ooh, ___ you're mak - ing me live, ___ what - ev - er this world can

give to me, ___ it's you, ___ you're all I ___ see, ___

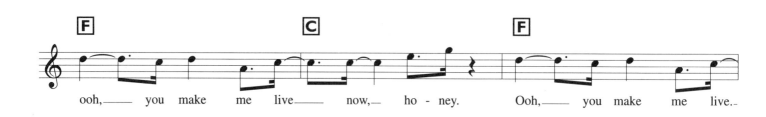

ooh, ___ you make me live ___ now, ho - ney. Ooh, ___ you make me live. _

___ Ah, ___ you're the best ___ friend ___ that I

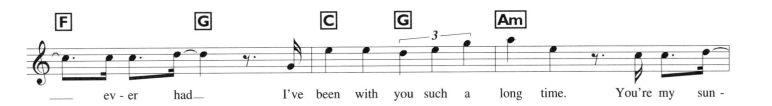

ev - er had— I've been with you such a long time. You're my sun -

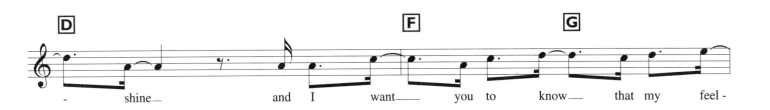

- shine— and I want— you to know— that my feel -

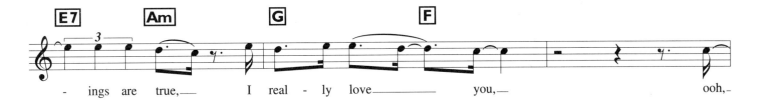

- ings are true,— I real - ly love— you,— ooh,—

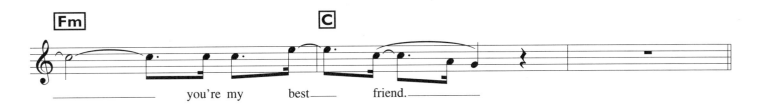

_____ you're my best— friend._____

Ooh,_____ you're mak - ing me live,— ooh I've been wan - - - der-ing

Still— come back to you, come rain or— shine— you've stood by me girl.— I'm
round,—

hap - - py at home.— You're my best friend.

EASIEST KEYBOARD COLLECTION

Easy-to-play melody line arrangements for all keyboards with chord symbols and lyrics. Suggested registration, rhythm and tempo are included for each song together with keyboard diagrams showing left-hand chord voicings used.

 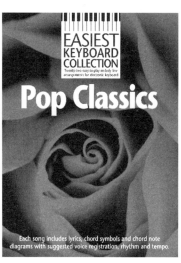 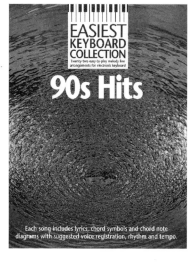 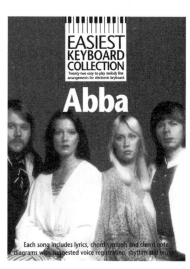

Showstoppers

Consider Yourself (Oliver!), Do You Hear The People Sing? (Les Misérables), I Know Him So Well (Chess), Maria (West Side Story), Smoke Gets In Your Eyes (Roberta) and 17 more big stage hits.
Order No. AM944218

Pop Classics

A Whiter Shade Of Pale (Procol Harum), Bridge Over Troubled Water (Simon & Garfunkel), Crocodile Rock (Elton John) and 19 more classic hit songs, including Hey Jude (The Beatles), Imagine (John Lennon), and Massachusetts (The Bee Gees).
Order No. AM944196

90s Hits

Over 20 of the greatest hits of the 1990s, including Always (Bon Jovi), Fields Of Gold (Sting), Have I Told You Lately (Rod Stewart), One Sweet Day (Mariah Carey), Say You'll Be There (Spice Girls), and Wonderwall (Oasis).
Order No. AM944229

Abba

A great collection of 22 Abba hit songs. Includes: Dancing Queen, Fernando, I Have A Dream, Mamma Mia, Super Trouper, Take A Chance On Me, Thank You For The Music, The Winner Takes It All, and Waterloo.
Order No. AM959860

Also available...

Ballads, Order No. AM952116 **The Corrs**, Order No. AM959849
The Beatles, Order No. NO90686 **Elton John**, Order No. AM958320
Boyzone, Order No. AM958331 **Film Themes**, Order No. AM952050
Broadway, Order No. AM952127 **Hits of the 90s,** Order No. AM955780
Celine Dion, Order No. AM959850 **Jazz Classics**, Order No. AM952061
Chart Hits, Order No. AM952083 **Love Songs**, Order No. AM950708
Christmas, Order No. AM952105 **Pop Hits**, Order No. AM952072
Classic Blues, Order No. AM950697 **60s Hits**, Order No. AM955768
Classics, Order No. AM952094 **80s Hits**, Order No. AM955779

...plus many more!